MST121
Using Mathematics

Chapter C2

Integration and modelling

About this course

This course, MST121 *Using Mathematics*, and the courses MU120 *Open Mathematics* and MS221 *Exploring Mathematics* provide a flexible means of entry to university-level mathematics. Further details may be obtained from the address below.

MST121 uses the software program Mathcad (MathSoft, Inc.) and other software to investigate mathematical and statistical concepts and as a tool in problem solving. This software is provided as part of the course.

This publication forms part of an Open University course. Details of this and other Open University courses can be obtained from the Student Registration and Enquiry Service, The Open University, PO Box 197, Milton Keynes, MK7 6BJ, United Kingdom: tel. +44 (0)870 333 4340, e-mail general-enquiries@open.ac.uk

Alternatively, you may visit the Open University website at http://www.open.ac.uk where you can learn more about the wide range of courses and packs offered at all levels by The Open University.

To purchase a selection of Open University course materials, visit the webshop at www.ouw.co.uk, or contact Open University Worldwide, Michael Young Building, Walton Hall, Milton Keynes, MK7 6AA, United Kingdom, for a brochure: tel. +44 (0)1908 858785, fax +44 (0)1908 858787, e-mail ouwenq@open.ac.uk

The Open University, Walton Hall, Milton Keynes, MK7 6AA.

First published 1997. Second edition 2003. Reprinted 2005, 2006.

Copyright © 2003 The Open University

Edited, designed and typeset by The Open University, using the Open University TEX System.

Printed in the United Kingdom by Thanet Press Ltd, Margate.

ISBN 0 7492 5554 4

2.3

Contents

Study guide

There are five sections in this chapter. They are intended to be studied consecutively in five study sessions. Each session requires two to three hours.

The pattern of study for each session might be as follows.

Study session 1:   Section 1.
Study session 2:   Section 2.
Study session 3:   Section 3.
Study session 4:   Section 4.
Study session 5:   Section 5.

Section 3 can be studied at any time after you have completed Section 1.

Subsection 1.2 requires the use of an audio cassette player. Subsection 4.2 will not be assessed. Section 5 requires the use of the computer together with Computer Book C.

Throughout this chapter it is often convenient to refer to a general function as $f(x)$ rather than f. This is a common abuse of notation.

> The optional Video Band C(iii), *Algebra workout — Integration*, could be viewed at any stage during your study of this chapter.

Introduction

In this chapter we continue to use calculus to model situations which involve continuous change. As explained in the Introduction to Block C, calculus has two main branches, called *differentiation* and *integration*. Chapter C1 was concerned with the first of these, and showed how the process of differentiation can be used to answer questions such as the following: How fast is something changing? Is it increasing or decreasing? Does it ever stop changing, permanently or temporarily?

In the Introduction to Block C, these questions were accompanied by two others: How does the change accumulate? How can the change be described by an equation? Study of the process of integration will enable us to answer the first of these questions, and to 'solve' equations of the type referred to in the second question, which are known as *differential equations*. However, the topic of differential equations is covered mainly in Chapter C3.

An example of 'accumulating change' is provided by the relationship between the velocity of a car and its position at any time. You saw in Chapter C1 that the instantaneous velocity of an object, such as a car, can be calculated by differentiating its position function with respect to time. We now consider instead the opposite situation, and ask how much can be deduced about the car's position from knowledge of its velocity function. Here the velocity is the rate of change of position, and the total change of position over some time interval is, roughly speaking, the accumulation of all the instantaneous changes which take place during the interval. It is integration which makes precise what is meant by an 'accumulation of instantaneous changes', and hence enables progress to be made. As suggested by this example, integration is a process which 'undoes' or reverses the effect of differentiation, and it is from this point of view that we start to study integration. The 'accumulation' aspect can be seen initially as a separate way of looking at integration, though there is a link between these two approaches which is of fundamental importance.

In Section 1 the idea of integration as an 'undoing' of differentiation is first introduced informally. The outcome of integrating a function is called an *integral* of that function and, in an audio-tape session, you will see how an integral can be determined for some standard functions. Section 2 shows how further integrals can be obtained using algebraic manipulation and the Composite Rule for differentiation, which you saw in Chapter C1.

In Section 3 you will see how integration plays an important part in analysing the motion of an object, by allowing first its *velocity* and then its *position* to be deduced from its *acceleration*. In particular, the case of constant acceleration is considered, which includes the basic model for objects falling under gravity.

In Section 4 a distinction is drawn between the *indefinite* integral considered so far and the *definite* integral. Correspondingly, the emphasis shifts from integration as the 'undoing' of differentiation to integration as an 'accumulation of changes'. You will see that one application of the definite integral is to find areas of regions which are bounded above by the graph of the function being integrated. This leads to the idea of an integral as an 'infinite sum'. In Section 5 you will see how the computer can be used to obtain both indefinite and definite integrals.

1   Basics of integration

To study Subsection 1.2, you will need an audio cassette player and Audio Tape 3.

The idea of integration as an 'undoing' of differentiation is introduced in Subsection 1.1. The outcome of integrating a function is called an *integral* of that function. You will see in Subsection 1.2 how an integral can be found for some standard functions. The techniques of integration are best assimilated through plenty of practice, so you will find that there is a good supply of activities to be worked through here.

1.1 *Undoing differentiation*

See Chapter C1, Subsection 1.3.

In Chapter C1 you saw that the velocity of an object moving in one dimension can be described by differentiating the function that describes the position of the object in terms of time. Suppose that the object P moves along the line shown in Figure 1.1, and that its position s (in metres) to the right of a fixed origin at time t (in seconds) is given by $s = 3t^2$.

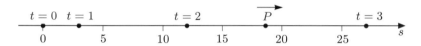

Figure 1.1   Moving object P

Then the velocity v of P at time t, which is the instantaneous rate of change of position, is

$$v = \frac{ds}{dt} = 6t \quad \text{(in metres per second, m\,s}^{-1}\text{)}.$$

Suppose now that the information given initially was not about the position of the object but about its velocity. If you are told only that P has velocity $v = 6t$, what can be said about its position as a function of time?

For example, the object might be a car, whose velocity is registered on its speedometer at each instant of time.

It is still the case that the position s and velocity v of P are linked by the equation $ds/dt = v$, so we seek an expression for s such that

$$\frac{ds}{dt} = 6t.$$

A solution to this equation is not hard to find because of the way in which the example was set up; the function $s = 3t^2$ is such a solution.

What we have done here is to 'undo' or 'reverse' the process of differentiation. This 'undoing' of differentiation can be regarded as a process in its own right, and it is called *integration*. The outcome of integrating is called an *integral*, so that $s = 3t^2$ is an integral of $ds/dt = 6t$.

This may seem straightforward so far, but matters can be harder to resolve when an integral is not effectively given in advance as it is in this case. For example, we might be told that an object is attached to the end of a spring, and oscillates with velocity $v = ds/dt = \cos t$. What position can the object have at time t?

On the basis of what you have seen about differentiation, you may be able to deduce that a possible position function in this case is $s = \sin t$, because $\cos t$ is the derivative of $\sin t$, but this requires more thought than the first example.

For the case of the object P, for which an integral $s = 3t^2$ was found above, the following question can be asked:

Is $s = 3t^2$ the *only* possible integral of $ds/dt = 6t$?

An alternative way of phrasing this question is as follows:

Is $s = 3t^2$ the *only* function whose derivative is $ds/dt = 6t$?

The activity below invites you to investigate this question.

Activity 1.1   What changes? What stays the same?

Differentiate each of the following position functions. What do you notice?

(a) $s = 3t^2$ (b) $s = 3t^2 + 2$ (c) $s = \sqrt{5} + 3t^2$ (d) $s = 3t^2 - \pi$

Solutions are given on page 56.

The outcome of Activity 1.1 suggests that there are many functions whose derivative is $ds/dt = 6t$, and that any function of the form $s = 3t^2 + c$, where c is a constant, has the same derivative. It turns out that this expression for s gives *all* the functions whose derivative is $6t$. We say that $s = 3t^2 + c$ is *the indefinite integral* of $ds/dt = 6t$.

This discussion demonstrates one respect in which integration is somewhat more than simply 'undoing differentiation'. On differentiating a given function we obtain a unique derivative, but on integrating a given function we are faced with an infinite family of possible functions.

In terms of the object P whose velocity is given as $ds/dt = 6t$, the position function must have the form $s = 3t^2 + c$, and this includes many possibilities besides the originally specified position function $s = 3t^2$ (for which $c = 0$). You will see in Section 3 how to choose a specific value for c that corresponds to a particular motion of the car.

Generalisation

We now generalise the mathematical developments described so far. Suppose that f is any function, and that F is a function whose derivative is equal to f; that is,

$$F'(x) = f(x) \quad \text{or} \quad \frac{d}{dx}(F(x)) = f(x). \tag{1.1}$$

In making general statements about integrals we shall typically use x to label the independent variable, rather than t (which stood for time above).

Then F is called **an integral** of f. As with the case above of position functions arising from a given velocity function, there is more than one possible choice for the function $F(x)$ which satisfies equation (1.1). If $F(x)$ is one such function, and c is any constant, then $F(x) + c$ also has derivative $f(x)$. This follows from the Sum Rule for derivatives, since we have

See Chapter C1, Subsection 3.2.

$$\frac{d}{dx}(F(x) + c) = \frac{d}{dx}(F(x)) + \frac{d}{dx}(c) = f(x) + 0 = f(x).$$

The expression $F(x) + c$, where c is any constant, represents all the functions whose derivative is $f(x)$. We call $F(x) + c$ **the indefinite integral** of $f(x)$. Since the constant c can take any value, it is described as an **arbitrary constant**, or as the **constant of integration**. The process of finding either an integral or the indefinite integral of a function is called **integration**.

Some texts use the words 'antiderivative' and 'primitive' for what we refer to here as an integral.

Thus, if $F(x)$ is any one function whose derivative is $f(x)$, then $F(x)$ is *an* integral of $f(x)$, whereas the expression $F(x) + c$, denoting all functions whose derivative is $f(x)$, is *the indefinite* integral of $f(x)$. This indefinite integral is denoted by $\int f(x)\, dx$, so we may write

$$\int f(x)\, dx = F(x) + c,$$

The collection of symbols

$$\int f(x)\, dx$$

is pronounced as 'the integral of f of x with respect to x' or simply as 'the integral of f of x dee-x'.

where c is an arbitrary constant.

When finding the indefinite integral of a function $f(x)$, it is natural to make the simplest possible choice for the function $F(x)$ (an integral of $f(x)$), and then to add the '$+c$' to this. This process is demonstrated in the following example.

Example 1.1   Finding an indefinite integral

Find the indefinite integral of the function $f(x) = 4x^3$.

Solution

Tables of derivatives were given at the ends of Subsections 3.1 and 4.3 in Chapter C1. The second of these is also in the Handbook.

We seek a function $F(x)$ whose derivative is equal to the given function $f(x) = 4x^3$. As you may recall from Chapter C1, we have

$$\frac{d}{dx}(x^4) = 4x^3,$$

so $F(x) = x^4$ is one possibility. There are others ($x^4 + 1$, for example), but x^4 is the simplest. Thus the indefinite integral of $f(x) = 4x^3$ is given by

$$\int 4x^3\, dx = x^4 + c,$$

where c is an arbitrary constant.

Comment

The answer $x^4 + c$ may be checked by differentiating it. The outcome should be (and is) the function $f(x) = 4x^3$ whose indefinite integral we set out to find. The indefinite integral of any other function can be checked in a similar way.

The effect of the indefinite integral operation

$$\int \ldots\, dx$$

The connection between integrals and sums will become apparent later in the chapter.

is to undo the effect of the differentiation operation represented by d/dx, including the addition of an arbitrary constant. The symbol $\int$ is called the **integral sign**. It is an old-fashioned elongated 'S', standing for the word 'sum'. The function which takes the place of the '$\ldots$' above is called the **integrand**, that is, the function to be **integrated**. The symbol dx on the end of the integral notation indicates that the integration in this case is to be performed with respect to the variable x.

As you have seen, integration can be performed with respect to variables other than x. For example,

$$\int \ldots du$$

represents an integration with respect to the variable u, which 'undoes' the effect of d/du. Thus, from the result of the integration in Example 1.1, we have

$$\int 4u^3 \, du = u^4 + c,$$

where c is an arbitrary constant.

This subsection has introduced the idea of integration as an 'undoing' of differentiation. The next embarks on the task of finding integrals for a variety of functions.

1.2 Integration by inspection

In Example 1.1, we integrated the function $f(x) = 4x^3$ by recalling that one function with derivative $4x^3$ is x^4. In other cases, the power of recall may not suffice to produce an integral, or the function to be integrated may not be in a form seen previously as the derivative of another function.

In such a situation, one important approach is to make an informed 'guess' at an answer! This is not as open-ended a proceeding as it might at first sound. Where it will work, the form of the original function suggests what type of guess to make. For example, knowing that an integral of $4x^3$ is x^4, we can 'guess' that an integral of the function $f(x) = x^3$ will be provided by some constant multiple of x^4. In fact, the appropriate multiple in this case is $\frac{1}{4}$, because

$$\frac{d}{dx}(\tfrac{1}{4}x^4) = \tfrac{1}{4}(4x^3) = x^3.$$

Here we use the Constant Multiple Rule for derivatives, from Chapter C1, Subsection 3.2.

Hence an integral of the function $f(x) = x^3$ is $\frac{1}{4}x^4$. It is often the case, as in this example, that the guess at an integral differs from the eventual answer by at most a constant multiple, and that the correct value of this multiple can be found rapidly by checking the derivative of the guess and then making an appropriate adjustment.

This 'guess and check' approach is profitable precisely because integration has the effect of 'undoing' differentiation, and because you have already built up a body of knowledge concerning derivatives. This knowledge can be called on, both as a source of clues while 'guessing' the appropriate form of function for an integral and in carrying out the check. The phrase 'guess and check' is not used in formal descriptions of this process, which is instead called integration *by inspection*.

In this subsection, you will see how integration by inspection can provide integrals for certain standard functions, leading to the construction of a table of basic integrals. You will also see that some of the rules for differentiation can be translated into rules for integration, which extend your ability to integrate beyond the results in the table.

Now listen to Audio Tape 3, Band 2, 'Integration by inspection'.

Frame 1

Reversing differentiation

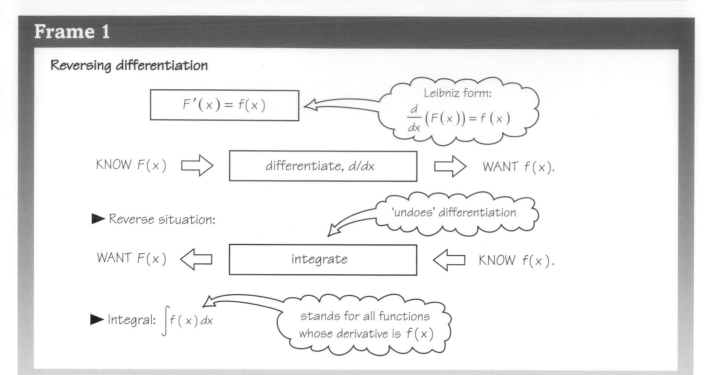

$F'(x) = f(x)$

Leibniz form:
$$\frac{d}{dx}(F(x)) = f(x)$$

KNOW $F(x)$ ⇒ differentiate, d/dx ⇒ WANT $f(x)$.

► Reverse situation:

'undoes' differentiation

WANT $F(x)$ ⇐ integrate ⇐ KNOW $f(x)$.

► Integral: $\int f(x)\,dx$ stands for all functions whose derivative is $f(x)$

Frame 2

Each function has many 'integrals'

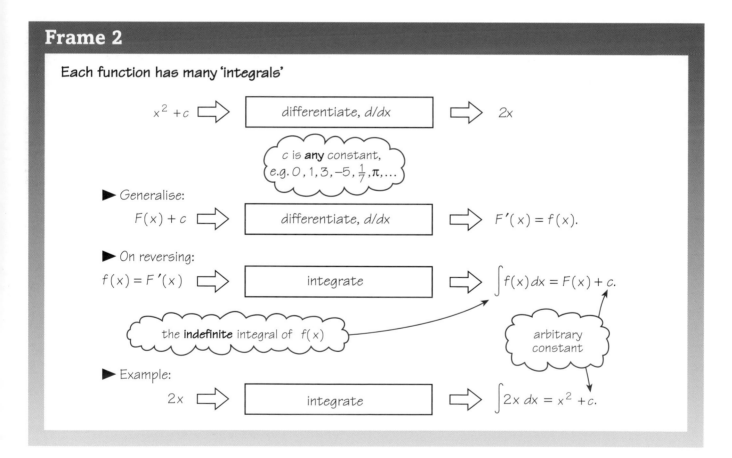

$x^2 + c$ ⇒ differentiate, d/dx ⇒ $2x$

c is **any** constant, e.g. $0, 1, 3, -5, \frac{1}{7}, \pi, \ldots$

► Generalise:

$F(x) + c$ ⇒ differentiate, d/dx ⇒ $F'(x) = f(x)$.

► On reversing:

$f(x) = F'(x)$ ⇒ integrate ⇒ $\int f(x)\,dx = F(x) + c$.

the **indefinite** integral of $f(x)$

arbitrary constant

► Example:

$2x$ ⇒ integrate ⇒ $\int 2x\,dx = x^2 + c$.

Frame 3

A table of derivatives

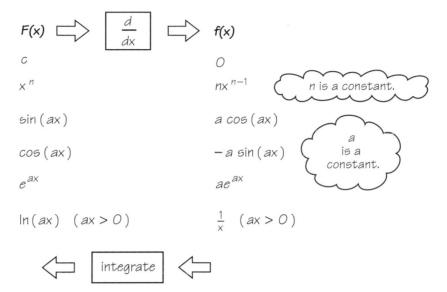

$F(x) \Rightarrow \boxed{\dfrac{d}{dx}} \Rightarrow f(x)$

$F(x)$	$f(x)$
c	0
x^n	nx^{n-1}
$\sin(ax)$	$a\cos(ax)$
$\cos(ax)$	$-a\sin(ax)$
e^{ax}	ae^{ax}
$\ln(ax) \quad (ax > 0)$	$\dfrac{1}{x} \quad (ax > 0)$

n is a constant.

a is a constant.

$\Leftarrow \boxed{\text{integrate}} \Leftarrow$

Frame 4

Using the table to integrate

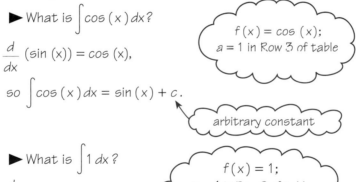

▶ What is $\int \cos(x)\,dx$?

$\dfrac{d}{dx}(\sin(x)) = \cos(x),$

so $\int \cos(x)\,dx = \sin(x) + c.$

*$f(x) = \cos(x)$;
$a = 1$ in Row 3 of table*

arbitrary constant

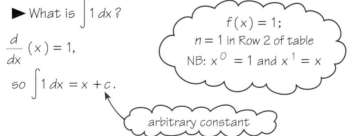

▶ What is $\int 1\,dx$?

$\dfrac{d}{dx}(x) = 1,$

so $\int 1\,dx = x + c.$

*$f(x) = 1$;
$n = 1$ in Row 2 of table
NB: $x^0 = 1$ and $x^1 = x$*

arbitrary constant

Frame 5

Three integrals for you to do

▶ What is $\int 3x^2\, dx$?

$\dfrac{d}{dx}\left(\boxed{}\right) = 3x^2$, so $\int 3x^2\, dx = \boxed{}$.

▶ What is $\int nx^{n-1}\, dx$?

$\dfrac{d}{dx}\left(\boxed{}\right) = nx^{n-1}$, so $\int nx^{n-1}\, dx = \boxed{}$.

> Special case $n = 0$: $\int 0\, dx = c$.

▶ What is $\int \dfrac{1}{x}\, dx$ (for $x > 0$)?

$\dfrac{d}{dx}\left(\boxed{}\right) = \dfrac{1}{x}$ $(a > 0, x > 0)$,

so $\int \dfrac{1}{x}\, dx = \boxed{}$.

> also expressible as $\ln(x) + c$, where $c = \ln(a)$

Frame 6

Integrals not in the table

▶ What is $\int x^4\, dx$?

> $5x^4$ is in table; nx^{n-1} with $n = 5$.

$\dfrac{d}{dx}\left(x^5\right) = 5x^4$.

> Use Constant Multiple Rule: $\dfrac{d}{dx}(bF(x)) = b\dfrac{d}{dx}(F(x))$.

Guess: **Check:**

$\dfrac{x^5}{5}$ $\dfrac{d}{dx}\left(\dfrac{x^5}{5}\right) = \dfrac{1}{5}\dfrac{d}{dx}\left(x^5\right) = \dfrac{1}{5}\left(5x^4\right) = x^4$.

So $\int x^4\, dx = \dfrac{x^5}{5} + c$.

▶ What is $\int \sin(x)\, dx$?

$\dfrac{d}{dx}(\cos(x)) = -\sin(x)$.   > from table

Guess: **Check:**

$-\cos(x)$ $\dfrac{d}{dx}(-\cos(x)) = -1 \times (-\sin(x)) = \sin(x)$.

So $\int \sin(x)\, dx = -\cos(x) + c$.

Frame 7

The integral of x^n

▶ What is $\int x^n \, dx$?

First guess:

x^{n+1}

Second guess:

[ ]

So $\int x^n \, dx =$ [ ] .

Check:

$\dfrac{d}{dx}\left(x^{n+1}\right) = (n+1)x^n$.

Replace n by $n+1$ in Row 2 of table.

Check:

[ ]

Does this hold for all n?

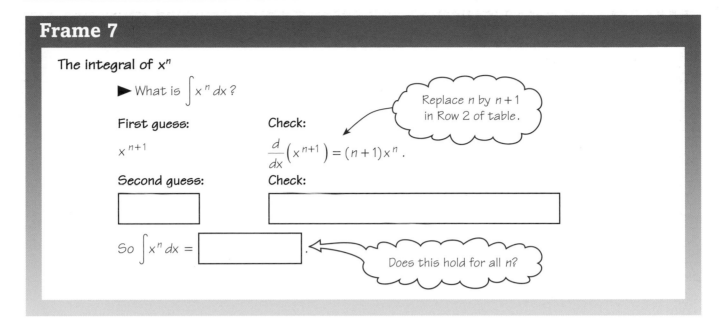

Frame 8

Two for you to try

▶ What is $\int e^{ax} \, dx$?

$\dfrac{d}{dx}\left(\boxed{}\right) = \boxed{}$ from table

Guess: [ ]   **Check:** [ ]

So $\int e^{ax} \, dx =$ [ ] . $a \neq 0$

▶ What is $\int \cos(ax) \, dx$?

$\dfrac{d}{dx}\left(\boxed{}\right) = \boxed{}$ from table

Guess: [ ]   **Check:** [ ]

So $\int \cos(ax) \, dx =$ [ ] . $a \neq 0$

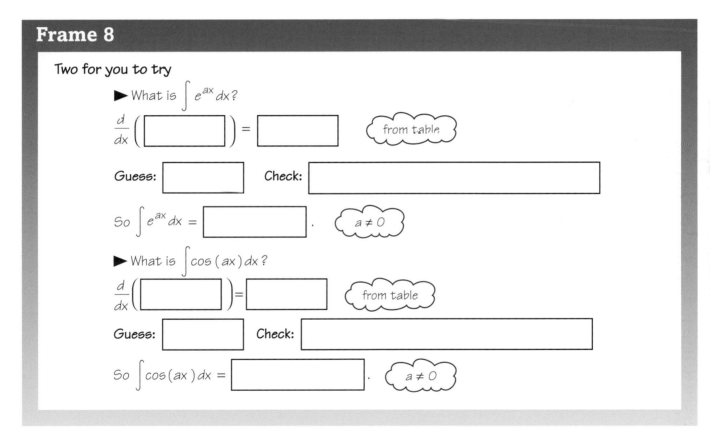

Frame 9

A table of integrals

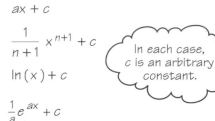

$f(x) \Rightarrow$ integrate $\Rightarrow \int f(x)\,dx$

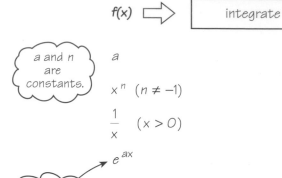

a and n are constants.

a $ax + c$

$x^n \;\; (n \neq -1)$ $\dfrac{1}{n+1} x^{n+1} + c$

$\dfrac{1}{x} \;\; (x > 0)$ $\ln(x) + c$

In each case, c is an arbitrary constant.

$a \neq 0$

e^{ax} $\dfrac{1}{a} e^{ax} + c$

$\cos(ax)$ $\dfrac{1}{a} \sin(ax) + c$

$\sin(ax)$ $-\dfrac{1}{a} \cos(ax) + c$

Frame 10

Combining results

▶ What is $\int (e^{3x} + \sin(6x))\,dx$?

From table:

(a) e^{3x} has an integral $\dfrac{1}{3} e^{3x}$;   [$a = 3$ in table]

(b) $\sin(6x)$ has an integral $-\dfrac{1}{6} \cos(6x)$.   [$a = 6$ in table]

Guess: $\dfrac{1}{3} e^{3x} - \dfrac{1}{6} \cos(6x)$

Check: $\dfrac{d}{dx}\left(\dfrac{1}{3} e^{3x} - \dfrac{1}{6} \cos(6x) \right)$

Sum Rule:
$$\dfrac{d}{dx}(F(x) + G(x)) = \dfrac{d}{dx}(F(x)) + \dfrac{d}{dx}(G(x)).$$

$$= \dfrac{d}{dx}\left(\dfrac{1}{3} e^{3x} \right) + \dfrac{d}{dx}\left(-\dfrac{1}{6} \cos(6x) \right)$$

$$= e^{3x} + \sin(6x).$$

OR $\int \left(e^{3x} + \sin(6x) \right) dx = \int e^{3x}\,dx + \int \sin(6x)\,dx$

$$= \dfrac{1}{3} e^{3x} - \dfrac{1}{6} \cos(6x) + c$$

only one arbitrary constant needed in answer

▶ What is $\int 5 \cos(x)\,dx$?

From table: $\cos(x)$ has an integral $\sin(x)$.

Guess: **Check:**

Constant Multiple Rule

$5 \sin(x)$ $\dfrac{d}{dx}(5 \sin(x)) = 5\dfrac{d}{dx}(\sin(x)) = 5\cos(x).$

OR $\int 5 \cos(x)\,dx = 5 \int \cos(x)\,dx$

$$= 5 \sin(x) + c$$

'+ c' is just as correct as '+ $5c$'

Frame 11

Rules for integrals

► Sum Rule: $\boxed{\displaystyle\int (f(x) + g(x))\,dx = \int f(x)\,dx + \int g(x)\,dx.}$

► Constant Multiple Rule: $\boxed{\displaystyle\int (bf(x))\,dx = b\int f(x)\,dx.}$

► Combined: $\boxed{\displaystyle\int (af(x) + bg(x))\,dx = a\int f(x)\,dx + b\int g(x)\,dx.}$

In Frame 9 you met a table of integrals, which is reproduced as Table 1.1.

Table 1.1

Function $f(x)$	Integral $\displaystyle\int f(x)\,dx$
a (constant)	$ax + c$
x^n $(n \neq -1)$	$\dfrac{1}{n+1}x^{n+1} + c$
$\dfrac{1}{x}$ $(x > 0)$	$\ln x + c$
e^{ax}	$\dfrac{1}{a}e^{ax} + c$
$\cos(ax)$	$\dfrac{1}{a}\sin(ax) + c$
$\sin(ax)$	$-\dfrac{1}{a}\cos(ax) + c$

This table is in the Handbook.

In each case, c is an arbitrary constant.

Note that e^{ax} can be written also as $\exp(ax)$. The constant a here, and in the entries for $\cos(ax)$ and $\sin(ax)$, can take any non-zero value.

The **Sum Rule** and **Constant Multiple Rule** for integrals are

$$\int (f(x) + g(x))\,dx = \int f(x)\,dx + \int g(x)\,dx, \tag{1.2}$$

$$\int bf(x)\,dx = b\int f(x)\,dx, \tag{1.3}$$

where b is any non-zero constant. These can be combined into the rule

$$\int (af(x) + bg(x))\,dx = a\int f(x)\,dx + b\int g(x)\,dx, \tag{1.4}$$

where a and b are any non-zero constants.

A similar rule can be written down for the integral of a sum of three or more constant multiples of functions.

Activity 1.2 More practice in applying the table and rules

Find each of the following indefinite integrals, using Table 1.1 and the rules for integration stated in equations (1.2)–(1.4), as appropriate.

(a) $\displaystyle\int \left(\frac{1}{x} + e^{3x}\right) dx$ $(x > 0)$ (b) $\displaystyle\int \left(3\sqrt{x} + \frac{8}{\sqrt{x}}\right) dx$ $(x > 0)$

(c) $\displaystyle\int (a\sin(\omega t) + b\cos(\omega t))\,dt$ (where a, b and ω are constants)

(d) $\displaystyle\int \left(\tfrac{2}{3}x^{5/3} - 5x^{-3/2} + 4e^{-2x}\right) dx$ $(x > 0)$

Solutions are given on page 56.

For cases where Table 1.1 applies, its use, with or without the Sum and Constant Multiple Rules, replaces any need to 'guess and check'.

Recall that $\sqrt{x} = x^{1/2}$ and that $1/\sqrt{x} = x^{-1/2}$.

The symbol ω is the Greek lower-case letter omega.

> ### Activity 1.3   Integrating two new functions
>
> Find each of the following indefinite integrals.
>
> (a) $\int \frac{1}{2}(e^x + e^{-x})\,dx$ (b) $\int \frac{1}{2}(e^x - e^{-x})\,dx$
>
> Solutions are given on page 56.
>
> ### Comment

These functions may be evaluated directly on a scientific calculator. Sometimes this involves pressing a 'hyp' key before the 'cos' or 'sin' key.

> The functions cosh and sinh (known as the *hyperbolic cosine* and *hyperbolic sine*, respectively) are defined by
>
> $$\cosh x = \tfrac{1}{2}(e^x + e^{-x}) \quad\text{and}\quad \sinh x = \tfrac{1}{2}(e^x - e^{-x}).$$
>
> Hence in this activity you have shown that
>
> $$\int \cosh x\,dx = \sinh x + c \quad\text{and}\quad \int \sinh x\,dx = \cosh x + c,$$
>
> which are equivalent to saying that $\sinh' = \cosh$ and $\cosh' = \sinh$.

Summary of Section 1

This section has introduced:

◇   integration as the 'undoing' of, or reverse process to, differentiation, together with the obtaining of a number of integrals;

◇   the indefinite integral of the function $f(x)$,

$$\int f(x)\,dx = F(x) + c,$$

where c is an arbitrary constant and $F(x)$ is *an* integral of $f(x)$, that is, any function whose derivative is $f(x)$;

◇   the approach to finding integrals by inspection;

◇   the integrals of some commonly-occurring functions, as listed in Table 1.1 on page 15;

You will be expected to be able to integrate any of these functions 'by hand', that is, without recourse to a calculator or computer.

◇   further integrals, which were found using the Constant Multiple Rule and Sum Rule for integration (see equations (1.2)–(1.4)).

Exercise for Section 1

Exercise 1.1

Find each of the following indefinite integrals, using Table 1.1 and the rules for integration stated in equations (1.2)–(1.4), as appropriate.

(a) $\int t^\pi\,dt$ (b) $\int \left(\frac{3}{y^4} + 5\sin(5y)\right)dy$ $(y > 0)$

(c) $\int 2\cos\left(\frac{s}{7}\right)ds$ (d) $\int \left(\frac{3}{v} + e^{4v}\right)dv$ $(v > 0)$ (e) $\int \frac{1}{2}e^{x/4}\,dx$

2 Further integration

In the previous section integration was introduced, and you saw how to obtain the indefinite integrals of a variety of functions. This section widens the range of functions that you will be able to integrate.

Subsection 2.1 indicates that basic algebraic rearrangements of the integrand can be effective, while Subsection 2.2 shows that the Composite Rule from Chapter C1 can assist in finding certain integrals.

2.1 Using algebraic rearrangements

Since the start of Block C you have been introduced to the processes of differentiation and integration, each of which involves new ideas, notation and algebraic rules. Faced with new mathematics, it is natural to concentrate on what has just been introduced, rather than on what was known and understood previously. However, basic algebra has an important part to play in applying calculus. The main message of this subsection is that integration can be facilitated by algebraic manipulations which are not themselves regarded as being within the scope of 'calculus'.

Given a function to be integrated, it is useful to express it in as simple a form as possible prior to integration. What 'simple' means in mathematics depends on the context. For example, consider the function

$$f(x) = x^2 - 4x + 3 = (x - 3)(x - 1).$$

The factorised form of $f(x)$ would be regarded as 'simpler' than the unfactorised form if the object was to find solutions of the equation $f(x) = 0$. For the purpose of integrating $f(x)$, on the other hand, the unfactorised (expanded) form is the simpler, since we have results that enable the integration of sums and constant multiples of powers of x.

Similar comments apply where division by a power of x is concerned. The function $g(x) = (x^6 + 1)/x$ $(x > 0)$ cannot be matched directly with entries in Table 1.1 on page 15, but it may readily be integrated after noting that

$$g(x) = \frac{x^6 + 1}{x} = \frac{x^6}{x} + \frac{1}{x} = x^5 + \frac{1}{x}.$$

This again is a sum of powers of x (since $1/x = x^{-1}$). The strategy of 'expressing the integrand in terms of powers of x' is also applicable where roots of x are present, as you saw in Activity 1.2(b).

Example 2.1 Finding indefinite integrals

Find the indefinite integral of each of the following functions.

(a) $f(x) = (x - 3)(x - 1)$

(b) $g(x) = \dfrac{x^6 + 1}{x}$ $(x > 0)$

(c) $h(x) = \dfrac{2x - 3}{\sqrt{x}}$ $(x > 0)$

Solution

(a) The indefinite integral of $f(x)$ is

$$\int (x-3)(x-1)\,dx = \int (x^2 - 4x + 3)\,dx$$
$$= \tfrac{1}{3}x^3 - 4(\tfrac{1}{2}x^2) + 3x + c$$
$$= \tfrac{1}{3}x^3 - 2x^2 + 3x + c,$$

where c is an arbitrary constant.

(b) The indefinite integral of $g(x)$ is

$$\int \frac{x^6 + 1}{x}\,dx = \int \left(x^5 + \frac{1}{x} \right)\,dx$$
$$= \tfrac{1}{6}x^6 + \ln x + c,$$

where c is an arbitrary constant.

(c) The indefinite integral of $h(x)$ is

$$\int \frac{2x - 3}{\sqrt{x}}\,dx = \int \left(\frac{2x}{x^{1/2}} - \frac{3}{x^{1/2}} \right)\,dx$$
$$= \int (2x^{1/2} - 3x^{-1/2})\,dx$$
$$= 2(\tfrac{2}{3}x^{3/2}) - 3(2x^{1/2}) + c$$
$$= \tfrac{4}{3}x^{3/2} - 6x^{1/2} + c,$$

where c is an arbitrary constant.

(This can also be written as

$$\tfrac{2}{3}\sqrt{x}(2x - 9) + c,$$

but, in general, there is no need to factorise such expressions.)

Here are some similar integrals for you to try.

Activity 2.1   Finding indefinite integrals

Find each of the following indefinite integrals, where $x > 0$ in parts (b) and (c).

In part (c), recall that $\sqrt[3]{x} = x^{1/3}$.

(a) $\displaystyle\int (x+1)^2\,dx$ (b) $\displaystyle\int \frac{x^2 + 1}{x^4}\,dx$ (c) $\displaystyle\int \sqrt[3]{x} \left(10x^2 - \frac{1}{x^2} \right)\,dx$

Solutions are given on page 56.

These rules are:

$$a^m \times a^n = a^{m+n},$$
$$a^m \div a^n = a^{m-n},$$
$$(a^m)^n = a^{mn}.$$

See Chapter A0, Subsection 3.1.

You have already seen the rules for combining powers put to use in manipulating expressions that involve powers of x. They also prove useful in dealing with functions that involve exponentials.

Example 2.2   Finding further indefinite integrals

Find the indefinite integral of each of the following functions.

(a) $f(x) = e^{3-x}$ (b) $g(x) = (e^{3x} - e^{-x})^2$

Solution

(a) The indefinite integral of $f(x)$ is

$$\int e^{3-x}\,dx = \int e^3 e^{-x}\,dx$$
$$= -e^3 e^{-x} + c$$
$$= -e^{3-x} + c,$$

where c is an arbitrary constant.

Note that e^3, being the cube of $e \simeq 2.718$, is a constant. Therefore the Constant Multiple Rule can be applied to this integral.

(b) The indefinite integral of $g(x)$ is

$$\int (e^{3x} - e^{-x})^2\,dx = \int \left((e^{3x})^2 - 2e^{3x}e^{-x} + (e^{-x})^2\right)\,dx$$
$$= \int \left(e^{6x} - 2e^{2x} + e^{-2x}\right)\,dx$$
$$= \tfrac{1}{6}e^{6x} - e^{2x} - \tfrac{1}{2}e^{-2x} + c,$$

where c is an arbitrary constant.

Here are some similar integrals for you to try.

Activity 2.2   *Finding further indefinite integrals*

Find each of the following indefinite integrals.

(a) $\displaystyle\int e^{2x-1}\,dx$ (b) $\displaystyle\int (2 + e^{x/2})(1 - e^{-x/2})\,dx$

Solutions are given on page 56.

Using trigonometric formulas

Sometimes trigonometric formulas permit an integrand to be manipulated algebraically into a form where the integral can be recognised from a standard table. As you may recall from Chapter A2, the formula

$$\cos^2\theta + \sin^2\theta = 1 \tag{2.1}$$

holds for all values of θ. A further result follows from this on dividing through by $\cos^2\theta$, for those values of θ such that $\cos\theta \neq 0$. This formula is

$$1 + \tan^2\theta = \sec^2\theta. \tag{2.2}$$

See Chapter A2, Subsection 3.1.

Both of these results have useful applications within calculus, as you will see soon. Further trigonometric formulas that have not previously been introduced in the course are now stated. These formulas express each of $\sin(2\theta)$ and $\cos(2\theta)$ in terms of $\sin\theta$ and $\cos\theta$, and are known as the *double-angle formulas*.

Double-angle formulas

The following formulas apply for any angle θ:

$$\sin(2\theta) = 2\sin\theta\cos\theta;$$

$$\cos(2\theta) = \cos^2\theta - \sin^2\theta = 2\cos^2\theta - 1 = 1 - 2\sin^2\theta.$$

A derivation of these formulas is given in the Appendix.

The second and third expressions for $\cos(2\theta)$ are obtained from the first, by noting from equation (2.1) that

$$\sin^2 \theta = 1 - \cos^2 \theta \quad \text{and} \quad \cos^2 \theta = 1 - \sin^2 \theta.$$

The usefulness of the double-angle formulas to calculus is that they often permit products of sines and cosines to be replaced by equivalent expressions that are easier to integrate. The following example and activity demonstrate this approach.

Example 2.3   Using double-angle formulas in integration

Find each of the following indefinite integrals.

(a) $\displaystyle\int \cos^2 x \, dx$ (b) $\displaystyle\int \cos\left(\tfrac{1}{2}x\right) \sin\left(\tfrac{1}{2}x\right) dx$

Solution

(a) From the second version of the double-angle formula for $\cos(2\theta)$, with $\theta = x$, we have

$$\cos(2x) = 2\cos^2 x - 1,$$

which can be rearranged to give

$$\cos^2 x = \tfrac{1}{2}(\cos(2x) + 1).$$

Hence the required indefinite integral is

$$\int \cos^2 x \, dx = \int \left(\tfrac{1}{2}\cos(2x) + \tfrac{1}{2}\right) dx$$
$$= \tfrac{1}{4}\sin(2x) + \tfrac{1}{2}x + c,$$

where c is an arbitrary constant.

(This answer can also be expressed, using the double-angle formula for $\sin(2\theta)$, as $\tfrac{1}{2}\sin x \cos x + \tfrac{1}{2}x + c$.)

(b) From the double-angle formula for $\sin(2\theta)$, with $\theta = \tfrac{1}{2}x$, we have

$$\int \cos\left(\tfrac{1}{2}x\right) \sin\left(\tfrac{1}{2}x\right) dx = \int \tfrac{1}{2}\sin x \, dx$$
$$= -\tfrac{1}{2}\cos x + c,$$

where c is an arbitrary constant.

Here are some similar integrals for you to try.

Activity 2.3   Using double-angle formulas in integration

(a) Using the third version of the double-angle formula for $\cos(2\theta)$, show that

$$\sin^2 x = \tfrac{1}{2}(1 - \cos(2x)).$$

Hence find the indefinite integral

$$\int \sin^2 x \, dx.$$

(b) By using the double-angle formulas for $\sin(2\theta)$ and $\cos(2\theta)$ in turn, show that

$$\sin^2 x \cos^2 x = \tfrac{1}{8}(1 - \cos(4x)).$$

Hence find the indefinite integral

$$\int \sin^2 x \cos^2 x \, dx.$$

Solutions are given on page 56.

Algebraic manipulation by itself will not always reduce the integrand to a form where an integral can be obtained from a standard table of integrals. However, when faced with a function $f(x)$ to integrate, it suffices to guess some function $F(x)$ whose derivative is $f(x)$. This process is similar to that referred to as 'guess and check' earlier, and is included under the heading of integration by inspection.

Activity 2.4   Using inspection and algebraic manipulation

(a) Use the Quotient Rule to find dy/dx when $y = \tan x$.

(b) Find the indefinite integral

$$\int \sec^2 x \, dx \quad (-\tfrac{1}{2}\pi < x < \tfrac{1}{2}\pi).$$

This repeats a differentiation which you carried out in Chapter C1, Subsection 4.2.

(c) By using equation (2.2) and the result from part (b), find the indefinite integral

$$\int \tan^2 x \, dx \quad (-\tfrac{1}{2}\pi < x < \tfrac{1}{2}\pi).$$

Solutions are given on page 57.

2.2   Using the Composite Rule

In this subsection the usefulness of integration by inspection is demonstrated further, but now we concentrate on cases where progress can be made by 'working back' from the Composite Rule. As you may recall, the Composite Rule states that

> if $k(x) = g(f(x))$, then $k'(x) = g'(f(x))f'(x)$.

The Composite Rule, also called the Chain Rule, was introduced in Chapter C1, Subsection 4.3.

In Leibniz notation, the corresponding statement is

> if $y = g(u)$, where $u = f(x)$, then $\dfrac{dy}{dx} = \dfrac{dy}{du}\dfrac{du}{dx}$.

We shall concentrate here on cases where the 'outer' function of the composite, $g(u)$, is either a power function or a logarithm function. The next activity involves such functions.

Activity 2.5   Integration by inspection again

(a) Use the Composite Rule to find dy/dx in each of the following cases.

(i) $y = (x^3 + 1)^5$ (ii) $y = \sin^3 x$ (iii) $y = \ln(x^2 + 1)$

(b) Use your answers to part (a) to find each of the following indefinite integrals.

(i) $\displaystyle\int x^2(x^3 + 1)^4 \, dx$ (ii) $\displaystyle\int \sin^2 x \cos x \, dx$ (iii) $\displaystyle\int \frac{x}{x^2 + 1} \, dx$

Solutions are given on page 57.

In Activity 2.5, the answers for the three integrals in part (b) were provided by the functions whose derivatives were obtained in part (a), apart from the need to multiply by an appropriate constant in each case. You might wonder how integration by inspection can work in similar instances where you are not 'given the answer' in this way.

In effect, this is done by recognising (where feasible) that the form of the integrand corresponds to an output from the Composite Rule. If the integrand can be identified as having the structure $g'(f(x))f'(x)$, for some choice of the functions f and g', then, by the Composite Rule, an integral will be $g(f(x))$. Recognising such a structure is easier in some cases than others, and we continue to restrict attention here to cases where the function g is either a power function or a logarithm function.

To generalise what was done in Activity 2.5, consider first a function of the form $k(x) = (f(x))^{n+1}$, where f is a smooth function and n is any real number. We can express k as a composite function of the form $k(x) = g(f(x))$ by letting g be the function with rule $g(u) = u^{n+1}$. Hence we have $g'(u) = (n+1)u^n$ so, according to the Composite Rule,

$$k'(x) = g'(f(x))f'(x) = (n+1)(f(x))^n f'(x).$$

In other words, we have

$$\frac{d}{dx}(f(x))^{n+1} = (n+1)(f(x))^n f'(x).$$

On dividing through by $n+1$ (for $n \neq -1$) and recalling that integration is the reverse of differentiation, we obtain the formula

$$\int (f(x))^n f'(x) \, dx = \frac{1}{n+1}(f(x))^{n+1} + c \quad (n \neq -1), \tag{2.3}$$

where c is an arbitrary constant.

A similar argument can be carried out, starting with the composite function $k(x) = \ln(f(x))$, where $f(x) > 0$. This leads to the formula

> Here we have $k(x) = g(f(x))$, where $g(u) = \ln u$ and hence $g'(u) = 1/u$.

$$\int \frac{f'(x)}{f(x)} \, dx = \ln(f(x)) + c \quad (f(x) > 0), \tag{2.4}$$

where c is an arbitrary constant.

Equation (2.4) deals with the case $n = -1$ which is excluded for equation (2.3), since $1/f(x) = (f(x))^{-1}$. Hence equations (2.3) and (2.4) together show how to integrate any function of the form $(f(x))^n f'(x)$. They illustrate how the Composite Rule may be 'used backwards' in order to recognise integrals.

> If $f(x) = x$, for which $f'(x) = 1$, then these equations give the same information as the second and third rows in Table 1.1 on page 15.

Two integration formulas

$$\int (f(x))^n f'(x)\, dx = \frac{1}{n+1}(f(x))^{n+1} + c \quad (n \neq -1) \qquad (2.3)$$

$$\int \frac{f'(x)}{f(x)}\, dx = \ln(f(x)) + c \quad (f(x) > 0) \qquad (2.4)$$

In each of these formulas, c is an arbitrary constant.

For example, consider once more the integrand $\sin^2 x \cos x$ which you integrated in Activity 2.5(b)(ii). Since $\cos x$ is the derivative of $\sin x$, this integrand can be written as $(f(x))^2 f'(x)$, where $f(x) = \sin x$. The corresponding indefinite integral can then be obtained from equation (2.3), on putting $n = 2$:

$$\int \sin^2 x \cos x\, dx = \tfrac{1}{3}\sin^3 x + c,$$

where c is an arbitrary constant.

The following example and activity relate to similar applications of equations (2.3) and (2.4).

When applying formula (2.4) in this chapter, you will not need to check the condition $f(x) > 0$, since in each case $f(x)$ will be positive either for all x or for all x in some given interval.

Example 2.4   Applying equations (2.3) and (2.4)

Find each of the following indefinite integrals.

(a) $\displaystyle\int x(x^2 - 1)^3\, dx$ (b) $\displaystyle\int \frac{e^{3x}}{e^{3x} + 1}\, dx$

Solution

(a) The factor x in the integrand is, except for a constant multiple, the derivative of $x^2 - 1$, so that we can apply equation (2.3) with $f(x) = x^2 - 1$ and $n = 3$. Since $f'(x) = 2x$, we write $x = \tfrac{1}{2}(2x)$ before applying the formula. Thus we have

$$\int x(x^2 - 1)^3\, dx = \tfrac{1}{2}\int (x^2 - 1)^3 (2x)\, dx$$
$$= \tfrac{1}{2} \times \tfrac{1}{4}(x^2 - 1)^4 + c$$
$$= \tfrac{1}{8}(x^2 - 1)^4 + c,$$

where c is an arbitrary constant.

The constant multiple $\tfrac{1}{2}$ is moved here from inside to outside the integral, in accordance with the Constant Multiple Rule. A similar step often occurs in other cases, including part (b) below.

(b) The numerator e^{3x} in the integrand is, except for a constant multiple, the derivative of the denominator $e^{3x} + 1$, so we can apply equation (2.4) with $f(x) = e^{3x} + 1$. Since $f'(x) = 3e^{3x}$, we write the numerator e^{3x} as $\tfrac{1}{3}(3e^{3x})$ before applying the formula. Thus we have

$$\int \frac{e^{3x}}{e^{3x} + 1}\, dx = \tfrac{1}{3}\int \frac{3e^{3x}}{e^{3x} + 1}\, dx$$
$$= \tfrac{1}{3}\ln(e^{3x} + 1) + c,$$

where c is an arbitrary constant.

Here are some similar cases for you to try.

Activity 2.6   Applying equations (2.3) and (2.4)

Find each of the following indefinite integrals.

(a) $\displaystyle\int x^2(8-x^3)^5\,dx$ (b) $\displaystyle\int \frac{x^2}{x^3-8}\,dx$ $(x>2)$

In part (c), recall that $\tan x = \sin x/(\cos x)$. In part (d), note that $f'(x)$ may be a constant function.

(c) $\displaystyle\int \tan x\,dx$ $(-\tfrac{1}{2}\pi < x < \tfrac{1}{2}\pi)$ (d) $\displaystyle\int (2x+5)^7\,dx$

Solutions are given on page 57.

To conclude this section, we return to the theme of Subsection 2.1. Sometimes, by writing integrands in alternative though algebraically equivalent forms, the applicability of equations (2.3) and (2.4) can be seen.

Activity 2.7   Integrating after rearrangement

(a) (i) By using equation (2.1), show that
$$\sin^3 x = \sin x - \cos^2 x \sin x.$$

(ii) Hence find the indefinite integral
$$\int \sin^3 x\,dx.$$

(b) By first multiplying top and bottom of the fraction in the integrand by x, find the indefinite integral
$$\int \frac{x}{x^2 - 1/x}\,dx \quad (x > 1).$$

Solutions are given on page 58.

Summary of Section 2

This section has introduced:

◇   more advanced examples of integration, including those facilitated by algebraic rearrangements which bring the integrand to a form where it can be integrated by inspection;

◇   rearrangement of integrands which involve trigonometric functions, using the double-angle formulas
$$\sin(2\theta) = 2\sin\theta\cos\theta,$$
$$\cos(2\theta) = \cos^2\theta - \sin^2\theta = 2\cos^2\theta - 1 = 1 - 2\sin^2\theta,$$

and the identities
$$\cos^2\theta + \sin^2\theta = 1,$$
$$1 + \tan^2\theta = \sec^2\theta;$$

◇   extension of integration by inspection to certain cases where the differentiation involves the Composite Rule, as described by equations (2.3) and (2.4).

Exercises for Section 2

Exercise 2.1

Find each of the following indefinite integrals.

(a) $\int t\sqrt{t}\,dt \quad (t > 0)$ (b) $\int e^{1+3x}\,dx$

(c) $\int x\left(x^3 + 2x^{-2/3} - \dfrac{1}{x}\right)dx \quad (x > 0)$ (d) $\int \cos^2(4u)\,du$

Exercise 2.2

Find each of the following indefinite integrals.

(a) $\int \sin x \cos^3 x\,dx$ (b) $\int \dfrac{x^2}{(x^3 + 1)^2}\,dx$

Exercise 2.3

(a) By first multiplying top and bottom of the fraction in the integrand by e^{-x}, and then applying equation (2.4), find the indefinite integral

$$\int \frac{e^{2x} - 1}{e^{2x} + 1}\,dx.$$

(b) Show that

$$\frac{e^{2x} - 1}{e^{2x} + 1} = 1 - \frac{2}{e^{2x} + 1}.$$

Hence find the indefinite integral

$$\int \frac{1}{e^{2x} + 1}\,dx.$$

(c) By first dividing top and bottom of the fraction in the integrand by x, and then applying equation (2.4), find the indefinite integral

$$\int \frac{1}{x \ln x}\,dx \quad (x > 1).$$

3 Modelling motion

The particle model for objects was introduced in Chapter B3, Subsection 4.1.

In this section we analyse the motion of an object in one dimension; that is, where the motion takes place along a single straight line in space. This can make sense only if the size of the object is neglected, which means that the object is modelled by a particle. Brief reference to motion of this type was made in Chapter C1, Subsection 1.3, and in Subsection 1.1 of this chapter. The study of motion, without reference either to the forces which cause it or to the mass of the moving object, is known as *kinematics*.

Subsection 3.1 gives a complete description of the relationships between *position*, *velocity* and *acceleration* in one-dimensional motion and shows how to apply these concepts in practical situations. Subsection 3.2 focuses on the particular case of motion with constant acceleration, for which useful general formulas can be derived that link the properties of the motion. These formulas are applied to a particular case study.

3.1 Position, velocity and acceleration

In order to describe the one-dimensional motion of a particle P which represents an object, we choose an axis to coincide with the straight line along which the particle travels. This choice amounts to deciding which of the two opposite directions along the line is to be regarded as positive, and which fixed point on the line is to be selected as an origin for the purpose of specifying where the particle is located. Figure 3.1 shows such an axis for motion along a horizontal line in the plane of the page.

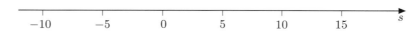

Figure 3.1 Axis for motion of particle P

The axis is labelled by the variable s. For a particular motion, s will vary with time t, and t is usually taken as the independent variable. The value of s at each time t is called the *position* of the particle at that time. The position s identifies both how far the particle is from the origin and in which direction it lies. The word *distance* is used to describe just the first of these, as detailed below.

Position and distance

◇ The **position** s of a particle, with respect to a chosen axis, is a measure of how far it is from the origin *and* of its direction relative to the origin.

◇ The **distance** $|s|$ of a particle from the origin is a measure of how far it is from the origin, irrespective of direction.

For example, the distance between $s_1 = 8$ and $s_2 = -7$ is

$$|8 - (-7)| = 15.$$

The concept of distance can be extended readily to any two points on the s-axis. If s_1 and s_2 are such points, then $|s_1 - s_2|$ is the distance between them.

We refer to the function that gives position s in terms of time t as the *position function* of the particle. This function can be represented by a graph of s against t, as illustrated for a particular position function in Figure 3.2(a).

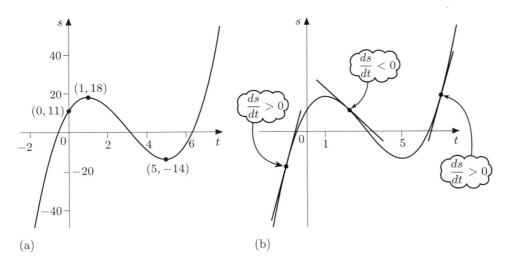

(a)   (b)

Figure 3.2   Graph of the position function $s = t^3 - 9t^2 + 15t + 11$

Using the graph, the motion can be described in words. The particle in this case arrives from the negative s-direction, passing through $s = 11$ at $t = 0$ and slowing down until $t = 1$, when it comes instantaneously to rest at $s = 18$. It then speeds up in the negative s-direction until $t = 3$, slows down once more, comes to rest instantaneously at $s = -14$ when $t = 5$, and finally heads off in the positive s-direction with increasing speed.

> Most of the values given in this paragraph are derived from consideration of the velocity and acceleration of the particle, as described later.

For any time t, we can consider the tangent to this graph (see Figure 3.2(b)). The gradient of this tangent is the instantaneous rate of change of s with respect to t, which is called the *velocity* v of the particle at that time. Hence we have $v = ds/dt$. When the velocity v is positive ($t < 1$ and $t > 5$), the particle is moving in the positive s-direction, whereas when v is negative ($1 < t < 5$), the particle moves in the negative s-direction. The word *speed* is used to describe just the magnitude of this rate of change, without the associated direction.

> $$v = \frac{ds}{dt} = 3t^2 - 18t + 15$$

> This is in contrast to everyday English, where 'speed' and 'velocity' mean much the same.

Velocity and speed

◇   The **velocity** $v = ds/dt$ of a particle is a measure of how fast it is moving *and* of its direction of motion.

◇   The **speed** $|v|$ of a particle is a measure of how fast it is moving, irrespective of its direction of motion.

The function that gives velocity v in terms of time t is called the *velocity function* of the particle. The velocity function can be represented by a graph of v against t. This is illustrated in Figure 3.3(a) for the same motion whose position function is shown in Figure 3.2(a). There are clear links between the graphs of the position and velocity functions. For example, the graph of v in Figure 3.3(a) is above the t-axis for values of t where the graph of s in Figure 3.2(a) is increasing, and the graph of v is below the t-axis for values of t where the graph of s is decreasing. The times $t = 1$ and $t = 5$, at which $v = 0$, are also the times at which the particle comes instantaneously to rest, as noted above.

> In Chapter B3, Subsection 2.2, (constant) velocity was introduced as a *vector* quantity in the context of motion in three dimensions. Since the motion here is one-dimensional, the velocity can be represented adequately by a *scalar*. A similar comment applies to position and acceleration.

The completed-square form of the velocity function is

$$v = 3(t-3)^2 - 12.$$

This shows that v has its least value, -12, when $t = 3$.

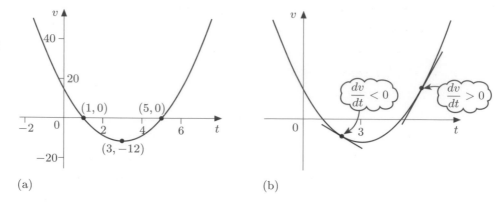

(a)   (b)

Figure 3.3   Graph of velocity function $v = 3t^2 - 18t + 15 = 3(t-1)(t-5)$

For any time t, we can consider the tangent to this graph (see Figure 3.3(b)). The gradient of this tangent is the instantaneous rate of change of v with respect to t, which is called the *acceleration* a of the particle at that time. Hence we have $a = dv/dt$.

$$a = \frac{dv}{dt} = 6t - 18$$

Acceleration

The **acceleration** $a = dv/dt$ of a particle is a measure of how fast its velocity is changing.

There is no separate word to describe the magnitude of the acceleration, $|a|$.

The function that gives the acceleration a in terms of time t is called the *acceleration function* of the particle. As with the position and velocity functions, the acceleration function can be represented by a graph, this time of a against t. Figure 3.4 illustrates this for the same motion whose position and velocity functions were shown in Figures 3.2 and 3.3, respectively.

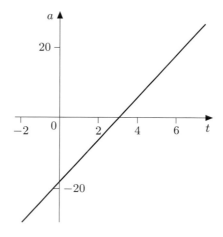

Figure 3.4   Graph of the acceleration function $a = 6t - 18 = 6(t-3)$

It is instructive to compare this graph with those of Figures 3.2(a) and 3.3(a). This comparison illustrates the following.

(a) If the particle is moving in the positive s-direction, so that $v > 0$ (which occurs for $t < 1$ or $t > 5$), then *positive* acceleration means that the particle speeds up ($t > 5$) while *negative* acceleration means that it slows down ($t < 1$).

A 'speeding up' motion is referred to as *accelerating*, while a 'slowing down' motion is *decelerating*.

(b) On the other hand, if the particle is moving in the negative s-direction, so that $v < 0$ (which occurs for $1 < t < 5$), then *positive* acceleration means that it slows down ($3 < t < 5$) while *negative* acceleration means that it speeds up ($1 < t < 3$).

At this point we note the SI units of measurement which are used for the kinematic quantities just introduced, and the usual abbreviations for these.

SI stands for 'Système International d'Unités', the system of units adopted for international usage in 1960.

SI units for kinematic quantities

◇ Time is measured in seconds (s).

◇ Position is measured in metres (m).

◇ Velocity is measured in metres per second ($\mathrm{m\,s^{-1}}$).

◇ Acceleration is measured in metres per second per second ($\mathrm{m\,s^{-2}}$).

From here on, you should assume that SI units are intended unless stated otherwise.

As you have seen, time t, position s, velocity v and acceleration a are related by the equations

$$v = \frac{ds}{dt} \quad \text{and} \quad a = \frac{dv}{dt}.$$

Since differentiation leads from position to velocity, and from velocity to acceleration, it is integration (the 'undoing' of differentiation) which leads in the reverse direction. However, as was pointed out in Subsection 1.1 in the case of the equation $ds/dt = v$, integration by itself gives an infinite family of possibilities for the position function, because of the constant of integration. Further information is needed in order to pin down a particular position function, and it is sufficient for this purpose to specify the position that the particle occupies at a given time. The same applies to finding a particular velocity function from the equation $dv/dt = a$, where the velocity at a given time can be used. The method of obtaining first the velocity and then the position from a given acceleration function is demonstrated in the following example.

Hence we also have

$$a = \frac{d}{dt}\left(\frac{ds}{dt}\right) = \frac{d^2 s}{dt^2}.$$

Example 3.1   Safe landing

The motion of a falling parachutist is modelled by a particle moving on an s-axis whose positive direction is vertically downwards. The origin for this axis corresponds to the point at which the parachute is opened, which occurs at time $t = 0$. According to the model, the acceleration function for the subsequent motion is

$$a = -27.5e^{-1.25t} \quad (t > 0).$$

(a) At the moment the parachute opens, the parachutist has velocity $30\,\mathrm{m\,s^{-1}}$. Find the velocity function of the parachutist for $t > 0$. What is the limiting speed of the parachutist as $t \to \infty$?

(b) Find the position function of the parachutist for $t > 0$.

Solution

(a) We have

$$\frac{dv}{dt} = a = -27.5e^{-1.25t} \quad (t > 0) \quad \text{and} \quad v = 30 \text{ when } t = 0.$$

Hence integration gives

$$v = \int (-27.5e^{-1.25t})\,dt = -27.5\left(\frac{1}{-1.25}\right)e^{-1.25t} + c$$
$$= 22e^{-1.25t} + c,$$

where c is an arbitrary constant.

The equation for dv/dt is called a *differential equation*, since it involves the derivative of an unknown function. You will see more about such equations in Chapter C3.

Putting $v = 30$ and $t = 0$ into this equation, we find that $30 = 22e^0 + c = 22 + c$, so $c = 8$. Hence, after the parachute opens, the velocity function is

$$v = 22e^{-1.25t} + 8 \quad (t > 0).$$

This limiting speed, for a falling object, is called the *terminal speed* of the object. While the limit $t \to \infty$ is never attained (the parachutist eventually reaches the ground!), the speed rapidly becomes very close to the terminal speed. For example, when $t = 10$,

$$v = 22e^{-12.5} + 8$$
$$\simeq 8.000\,08.$$

Since $\lim_{t \to \infty} e^{-1.25t} = 0$, the limiting speed is $\lim_{t \to \infty} |v| = 8\,\mathrm{m\,s^{-1}}$.

(b) On integrating

$$\frac{ds}{dt} = v = 22e^{-1.25t} + 8 \quad (t > 0),$$

we obtain

$$s = \int (22e^{-1.25t} + 8)\,dt = 22\left(\frac{1}{-1.25}\right)e^{-1.25t} + 8t + c$$
$$= -17.6e^{-1.25t} + 8t + c,$$

where c is an arbitrary constant.

However, due to the stated choice of origin, we have $s = 0$ when $t = 0$, so $0 = -17.6e^0 + 8 \times 0 + c$; that is, $c = 17.6$ (a different constant from that labelled as c in part (a)). We conclude that, after the parachute opens, the position function is

$$s = -17.6e^{-1.25t} + 8t + 17.6$$
$$= 17.6(1 - e^{-1.25t}) + 8t \quad (t > 0).$$

In the next activity, you can try a similar problem for yourself.

Activity 3.1   Free fall in a bungee jump

The motion of a falling person attached to one end of a bungee (elastic rope) is modelled by a particle moving on an s-axis whose positive direction is vertically downwards. The origin for this axis corresponds to the launch platform for the person. The other end of the bungee is attached to the launch platform. Assuming that air resistance is ignored, the acceleration function for the free-fall phase of the motion, before the bungee starts to stretch, is $a = 10\,\mathrm{m\,s^{-2}}$.

Here $10\,\mathrm{m\,s^{-2}}$ is a convenient approximation to the magnitude of the acceleration due to gravity, which is $g = 9.8\,\mathrm{m\,s^{-2}}$ to 1 decimal place.

In one particular jump, a bungee that is 30 metres long when unstretched is used.

(a) Suppose that the person drops off the launch platform at time $t = 0$, and hence has initial velocity zero. Find the corresponding velocity function for the free-fall phase of the motion.

(b) Obtain an expression for the corresponding position function.

(c) Find the time at which the bungee starts to stretch, and the speed of the person at this time.

Solutions are given on page 58.

Activity 3.1 concerned a motion in which the acceleration is constant. We continue to consider such motions in the next subsection.

3.2 Motion with constant acceleration

Most of this subsection is concerned with a practical problem which is of importance to any driver of a vehicle, and for which an informative solution can be obtained using mathematical modelling.

Firstly, however, we generalise the mathematics used in Activity 3.1, where you found the velocity and position functions of a particle representing a bungee jumper in free fall, starting from the acceleration due to gravity. This generalisation will then be put to use in setting up the model which follows.

Suppose that a particle moves along a straight line, on which an s-axis (with a positive direction and an origin) has been chosen. Suppose also that the particle has an acceleration a (in $\mathrm{m\,s^{-2}}$) which remains *constant* throughout the motion.

The motion of a bungee jumper while in free fall gives one example of such a motion, with $a = 9.8\,\mathrm{m\,s^{-2}}$. However, in what follows, the value of a need not necessarily be positive. If a is negative then, as long as the particle is moving in the positive s-direction, it is *decelerating*.

In Activity 3.1 this value was approximated by $a = 10\,\mathrm{m\,s^{-2}}$.

The acceleration is the derivative of the velocity v (in $\mathrm{m\,s^{-1}}$), so

$$\frac{dv}{dt} = a \quad \text{(constant).}$$

Integration gives

$$v = \int a\,dt = at + c,$$

where c is an arbitrary constant. Now c is the value of v when $t = 0$, and in recognition of this, we write it as the constant v_0, to obtain

$$v = at + v_0. \tag{3.1}$$

The velocity is the derivative of the position s (in metres), so

$$\frac{ds}{dt} = at + v_0.$$

Integration gives

$$s = \int (at + v_0)\,dt = \tfrac{1}{2}at^2 + v_0 t + c,$$

where c is an arbitrary constant. Here c is the value of s when $t = 0$, and in recognition of this, we write it as the constant s_0, to obtain

$$s = \tfrac{1}{2}at^2 + v_0 t + s_0. \tag{3.2}$$

The two equations (3.1) and (3.2) give expressions for the velocity and position of any particle moving in one dimension with constant acceleration.

Note that in the special case when the object starts from the chosen origin with zero velocity, that is, when $s_0 = v_0 = 0$, equations (3.1) and (3.2) reduce to

$$v = at \quad \text{and} \quad s = \tfrac{1}{2}at^2.$$

With $a = g \simeq 9.8\ \mathrm{m\,s^{-2}}$, these formulas describe the downward motion of a particle which falls under gravity alone, starting from rest at the origin.

In this case, the direction of the s-axis is vertically downwards.

We move next to the practical problem mentioned at the start of the subsection, for which the mathematical results just derived assist in obtaining a solution.

How far before you can stop?

In what follows, we apply once more the framework for mathematical modelling which was introduced in Chapter A1, Section 7.

When driving a car, you need to be aware of the distance ahead within which you can come to a halt safely by braking. This raises the question of just what is the minimum stopping distance required for safety purposes. Mathematical modelling can be brought to bear on this question. The results of any model should, of course, be treated cautiously, given the possible consequences of error. A safety margin can be added if such results are to be published or otherwise put into practice.

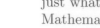

In order to start modelling, we need to specify the purpose of the model. The purpose in this case is to obtain the minimum distance within which a car can be brought to a halt. However, this distance is clearly dependent on other features of the situation, such as the velocity of the car when the brakes are first applied and the magnitude of the deceleration produced by the brakes. Leaving the second of these on one side for the moment, we specify the purpose of the model as follows:

◇   to obtain the minimum distance within which a car can be brought to a halt, in terms of its initial velocity (that is, the velocity when the brakes are first applied).

In order to create a mathematical model to address this problem, we make the following simplifying assumptions.

◇   While the car is braking, it can be represented by a particle that travels in a horizontal straight line. (Thus the road is flat and straight, and motion from one lane to another is not attempted.)

◇   The acceleration of the car while braking (a deceleration) is constant.

Under these assumptions, it is possible to apply equations (3.1) and (3.2) to this situation. We choose the s-axis to point in the direction in which the car is moving, with the origin at the point where the brakes are first applied. While braking occurs, the following quantities are relevant:

◇ t, the time since the brakes were first applied, in seconds;

◇ s, the position of the car at time t, in metres;

◇ v, the velocity of the car at time t, in $\mathrm{m\,s^{-1}}$;

Since the car decelerates, while v is positive for the chosen direction of motion, the value of a is negative.

The magnitude of a is determined by the braking force, so a larger value of $|a|$ corresponds to 'harder braking'.

◇ a, the constant acceleration of the car, in $\mathrm{m\,s^{-2}}$.

When the brakes are first applied, we have $t = 0$, $s = s_0 = 0$ and $v = v_0$. We also denote the time taken to stop after the brakes are applied by T, and the corresponding distance travelled by S, so that $t = T$ and $s = S$ when $v = 0$. All of the important quantities are included in Figure 3.5.

Due to artistic license, the particle continues to resemble a car!

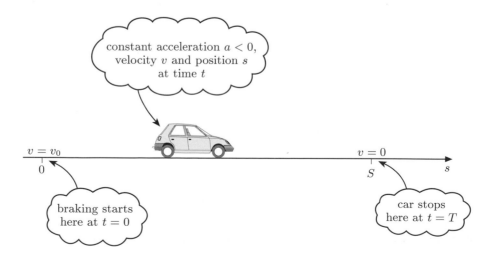

Figure 3.5   Braking car

The notation has been chosen to agree with that used in deriving equations (3.1) and (3.2), so these may now be stated:

$$v = at + v_0,$$ (3.1)

$$s = \tfrac{1}{2}at^2 + v_0 t + s_0.$$ (3.2)

From the choice of origin for the s-axis, we have

$$s_0 = 0.$$ (3.3)

At the instant when the car comes to a halt, we have

$$v = 0 \quad \text{and} \quad s = S \quad \text{when } t = T.$$ (3.4)

This completes the formulation of the mathematical model. The purpose of the model was stated to be

to obtain the minimum distance within which a car can be brought to a halt, in terms of its initial velocity.

First we find the stopping distance S in terms of the initial velocity v_0. On putting $t = T$ into equations (3.1) and (3.2), and using equations (3.3) and (3.4), we obtain

Do mathematics

$$0 = aT + v_0, \quad S = \tfrac{1}{2}aT^2 + v_0 T.$$

We can now relate S to v_0 by eliminating the unknown time T between these two equations. The first equation gives

$$T = -\frac{v_0}{a},$$

so the second equation gives

$$S = \tfrac{1}{2}a \left(-\frac{v_0}{a} \right)^2 + v_0 \left(-\frac{v_0}{a} \right)$$

$$= \frac{v_0^2}{2a} - \frac{v_0^2}{a} = -\frac{v_0^2}{2a}.$$

We have reached the equation

$$S = -\frac{v_0^2}{2a},$$ (3.5)

which relates the stopping distance S to the initial velocity v_0 as required, with the constant acceleration a appearing as a parameter in the equation.

Remember that $a < 0$. This explains the presence of the minus sign here and in the equation for T above.

At this stage of the mathematical modelling cycle, we need to interpret the results. This can be carried out on both a qualitative and quantitative level. For example, one way of interpreting equation (3.5) qualitatively is to treat v_0 and S now as variables and to sketch the graph of S against v_0 for a fixed value of a, as shown in Figure 3.6.

Interpret results

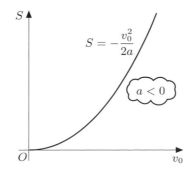

Figure 3.6 Graph of stopping distance against initial velocity

Recall that the braking force determines the deceleration.

It follows from equation (3.5) that the stopping distance increases as the square of the initial velocity. Thus the effect of doubling the initial velocity, for a given braking force, is to increase the stopping distance fourfold.

It is also clear from equation (3.5) that, for a fixed initial velocity, the stopping distance is inversely proportional to the magnitude of the acceleration, so stopping distance is minimised by applying the greatest possible braking force. This prediction seems very reasonable!

For a quantitative interpretation, we need to insert some numerical value for the acceleration a, and suitable data are available. Most cars with brakes in good condition can achieve a braking force corresponding to $a = -8 \text{ m s}^{-2}$, though the minimum requirement for passing the annual UK vehicle test corresponds to only $a = -5 \text{ m s}^{-2}$. The UK Highway Code gives a table of stopping distances which are based on an acceleration of about $a = -6.56 \text{ m s}^{-2}$.

Taking this last figure for illustrative purposes, we can evaluate the stopping distance S, from equation (3.5), for any desired value of the initial velocity v_0. For example,

$$\text{if } v_0 = 30, \text{ then } S = \frac{30^2}{2 \times 6.56} \simeq 69,$$

30 m s^{-1} is 108 kilometres per hour, or about 67 miles per hour.

so the stopping distance for an initial velocity of 30 m s^{-1} is predicted to be about 69 metres.

Evaluate

Having interpreted the results, we reach the modelling stage of evaluating the outcome. It was pointed out at the start that the results of such a model should be interpreted with caution, and the need for this is emphasised by the variation in values which could be chosen for the acceleration a. The Highway Code value seems quite conservative when compared with the figure quoted for brakes in good condition, but in either case one might expect a significant reduction in braking performance in wet conditions.

The Highway Code model for stopping distances includes an important element which we have not yet considered, and that is the reaction time of the driver. There is an appreciable time lag between the first realisation that braking is required and the actual application of the brakes, and an improved model for the stopping distance needs to take this into account. If the driver takes r seconds to react, then he/she travels a distance rv_0 metres before the brakes are applied. Adding this distance to the right-hand side of equation (3.5) gives the amended model

$$S = rv_0 - \frac{v_0^2}{2a}$$

for the stopping distance. The Highway Code assumes a reaction time of about 0.7 seconds. For the initial velocity 30 m s^{-1} considered before, the effect of including this reaction time is to increase the predicted overall stopping distance from 69 metres to 90 metres.

That concludes our mathematical modelling for the problem of predicting safe stopping distances. However, there is one mathematical feature encountered above which is worth expanding on. In order to relate S to v_0, we eliminated the time T between two equations. This step can be generalised, and the outcome is particularly useful in cases where we wish to relate velocity and position without explicitly involving the time. You are invited to derive the general result in the next activity.

Activity 3.2   No time!

A particle moving along the s-axis with constant acceleration a satisfies the two equations

$$v = at + v_0, \tag{3.1}$$
$$s = \tfrac{1}{2}at^2 + v_0 t + s_0. \tag{3.2}$$

By eliminating the time t between these two equations, obtain a direct relationship between the position s and velocity v of the particle. Hence show that

$$v^2 - 2as = v_0^2 - 2as_0.$$

A solution is given on page 59.

The result which you have just obtained states that the quantity

$$v^2 - 2as$$

remains constant throughout the motion since, at any time, it is equal to its initial value $v_0^2 - 2as_0$. This result ranks in importance alongside equations (3.1) and (3.2).

Motion with constant acceleration

The following formulas apply for the motion of a particle along a straight line with constant acceleration a, if at time $t = 0$ the particle has velocity v_0 and position s_0.

◇   The velocity v of the particle is given by

$$v = at + v_0. \tag{3.1}$$

◇   The position s of the particle is given by

$$s = \tfrac{1}{2}at^2 + v_0 t + s_0. \tag{3.2}$$

◇   The velocity and position of the particle are related by the equation

$$v^2 - 2as = v_0^2 - 2as_0. \tag{3.6}$$

These equations are often expressed as

$$v = u + at,$$
$$s = ut + \tfrac{1}{2}at^2,$$
$$v^2 = u^2 + 2as,$$

where $v_0 = u$ and $s_0 = 0$.

A direct application of equation (3.6) would have shortened our working in setting up and solving the mathematical problem for car stopping distances. Since $s_0 = 0$, and $s = S$ when $v = 0$, equation (3.6) gives

$$S = -\frac{v_0^2}{2a} \tag{3.5}$$

once more.

Equation (3.6) is particularly useful for models involving constant acceleration in which the main variables are position and velocity. If time appears explicitly in the problem, then one of equations (3.1) or (3.2) must be applied. These points are illustrated in the next example and activity.

Example 3.2 Dropping like a stone

The height of the Eiffel Tower is 300 metres. Suppose that a stone is dropped from rest at the top of the tower and falls directly to the ground. Ignoring air resistance, the acceleration of the stone is $a = g \simeq 10 \text{ m s}^{-2}$.

(a) Estimate the speed of the stone as it hits the ground.

(b) How long does the stone take to reach the ground?

Solution

(a) Choose the s-axis to point vertically downwards, with the origin at the top of the tower, and assume that the stone is modelled by a particle that moves on this axis. At time $t = 0$ the stone is released from rest, that is, with zero velocity, at the origin; hence we have $v_0 = 0$ and $s_0 = 0$. Equation (3.6) therefore gives

$$v^2 - 2 \times 10 s = 0$$

for the motion of the dropping stone. The stone hits the ground at $s = 300$, at which point its speed (and velocity) is

$$v = \sqrt{2 \times 10 \times 300} \simeq 77 \text{ m s}^{-1}.$$

(b) To find the value of t when the stone hits the ground, we need to use either equation (3.1) or equation (3.2), and the first of these is the simpler to apply. For the value of v just calculated, we have

$$t = \frac{v - v_0}{a} = \frac{\sqrt{2 \times 10 \times 300} - 0}{10} \simeq 7.7 \text{ seconds}.$$

Activity 3.3 Braking again

An aircraft touches down with a speed of 70 m s^{-1} at the start of a runway whose length is 550 metres. The pilot is required to reduce the speed of the aircraft to at most 5 m s^{-1}, prior to reaching the end of the runway.

At a speed of at most 5 m s^{-1}, it is safe for the aircraft to taxi off the runway.

(a) Calculate the minimum magnitude of the constant acceleration (deceleration) during braking which will achieve this requirement.

(b) When braking with this deceleration, how long does it take the aircraft to travel the length of the runway?

Solutions are given on page 59.

Summary of Section 3

This section has introduced:

◇ the links (provided by calculus) between position, velocity and acceleration, for a particle in one-dimensional motion;

◇ the following formulas which apply to the position s and velocity v of a particle moving along a straight line with constant acceleration a, when at time $t = 0$ the particle has position s_0 and velocity v_0:

$$v = at + v_0; \quad s = \tfrac{1}{2}at^2 + v_0 t + s_0; \quad v^2 - 2as = v_0^2 - 2as_0.$$

Exercises for Section 3

Exercise 3.1

A ball is projected vertically upwards with speed $25\,\mathrm{m\,s^{-1}}$. Its subsequent motion is to be modelled by ignoring air resistance and taking the magnitude of the acceleration due to gravity to be $g \simeq 10\,\mathrm{m\,s^{-2}}$.

(a) What is the maximum height attained by the ball above its point of projection? (Choose the s-axis to point vertically upwards, with origin at the point of projection. Note that the acceleration will then be negative.)

(b) How long does the ball take to return to the point of projection?

(c) At what times is the ball 20 metres above its point of projection?

Exercise 3.2

In a bungee jump, the initial period of free fall is followed by a phase of motion in which the jumper is pulled upwards by the stretched bungee. This question is about a model for this second phase of the motion, for a bungee whose unstretched length is 30 metres.

A model for the free-fall phase of a jump with such a bungee was considered in Activity 3.1.

As before, the falling person attached to the bungee is modelled by a particle moving on an s-axis whose positive direction is vertically downwards, and the origin for this axis corresponds to the launch platform for the person. However, the time is now measured from the moment at which the bungee starts to stretch, so that we have

$$s = 30 \quad \text{and} \quad v = 10\sqrt{6} \quad \text{when} \quad t = 0.$$

This value for the velocity v at the end of the free-fall phase was obtained in Activity 3.1.

One model of the situation after the bungee starts to stretch is given by the acceleration function

$$a = -50\sin(2t - \theta) \quad (t > 0),$$

where $\theta = \arcsin(\frac{1}{5})$. (This value for the constant θ ensures that the expression for a equals $g \simeq 10\,\mathrm{m\,s^{-2}}$ when $t = 0$. The acceleration has this value, due to the effect of gravity alone, until the bungee starts to stretch.)

(a) Use the Composite Rule to show that

$$\frac{d}{dt}(\cos(2t - \theta)) = -2\sin(2t - \theta); \quad \frac{d}{dt}(\sin(2t - \theta)) = 2\cos(2t - \theta).$$

(b) Using the first result from part (a), show that the velocity function for the period when the bungee is stretched is

$$v = 25\cos(2t - \theta) \quad (t > 0).$$

(Here you will need to use the fact that

$$\theta = \arcsin(\tfrac{1}{5}) = \arccos(\tfrac{2}{5}\sqrt{6}),$$

which follows from the triangle in Figure 3.7.)

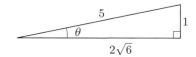

(c) Using the second result from part (a), show that the position function for the period when the bungee is stretched is

$$s = 12.5\sin(2t - \theta) + 32.5 \quad (t > 0).$$

Figure 3.7   A right-angled triangle

(d) What is the length of the bungee at full stretch?

(e) What is the largest magnitude of acceleration experienced by the jumper, and for what value of s does this occur?

In fact, the formulas for a, v and s hold only until $t = \frac{1}{2}\pi + \theta$, after which the particle has 'bounced back' and the bungee becomes slack once again.

4 Definite integrals, areas and summations

You have seen, in Sections 1 and 2, that integration is the 'undoing' of differentiation. In this section we investigate another aspect of integration, which on the face of it looks very different from the first. This involves seeing integration as a process related to the summation of a number of terms, in the limit as that number tends to infinity. The connection between this and our original view of integration is of importance both mathematically and from a practical point of view.

This link is explained by considering how to find the areas under the graphs of functions. Subsection 4.1 shows how such areas can be found using integration, while Subsection 4.2, which is non-assessed, explains how these areas can be calculated as a limit of summations.

4.1 Areas under graphs and the definite integral

It is often necessary in a practical situation to estimate the extent of an area. For example, building regulations refer to the ground area to be occupied by a piece of land or a building, so the extent of such areas must be apparent from a building plan. When a surface is to be painted, the painter needs to know how much paint is required to do the job, and this depends on the area of the surface.

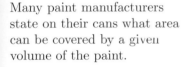
Many paint manufacturers state on their cans what area can be covered by a given volume of the paint.

Sometimes an area on a diagram is used to represent another type of physical quantity. For example, in Block D you will see cases where areas bounded above by the graph of a function represent the probabilities of certain events taking place.

By a *region* we mean a two-dimensional set with a boundary. In some courses, the word region has other meanings.

When a region is bounded by segments of straight lines, the calculation of its area is relatively simple. All such calculations depend ultimately on the formula for the area of a rectangle, which is bh for a rectangle with base b and height h. The area of a triangle can be seen to be half that of a rectangle with the same base and height. If the triangle has base b and height h, then its area is $\frac{1}{2}bh$. More general regions which are bounded by straight lines can be regarded as being made up of a number of triangular regions.

It is harder to calculate areas when part or all of the boundary of the region is curved. An example is shown in Figure 4.1(a), where the region of interest is bounded by straight lines on three sides, but by the graph of a non-linear function f on the fourth.

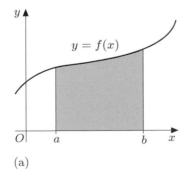

(a)

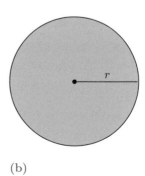

(b)

Figure 4.1   Areas of regions with curved boundaries

Another example, shown in Figure 4.1(b), is the area of a circle. No doubt you are aware that the area of a circle of radius r is πr^2, but where does this formula come from? You will see an answer to this question in Exercise 4.3.

The approach in this subsection is as follows. Firstly you are asked to find the areas of a couple of regions which are made up of rectangles and triangles, but for each of which an application of integration can be shown to give the same answer. Building on these results, it is argued that integration provides a means of calculating areas of the type shown in Figure 4.1(a), for any continuous function f. Then we look at the application of this integration approach in a variety of cases where f is a non-linear function.

Activity 4.1   Area of a rectangle

(a) What is the area of the region under the graph of the function $f(x) = 3$ and above the x-axis, between the lines $x = 0$ and $x = 5$ (see Figure 4.2)?

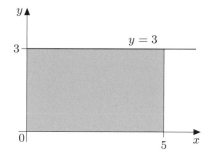

Figure 4.2   A rectangular area

(b) Choose an integral F of the function f given in part (a), and evaluate $F(5) - F(0)$. What do you notice?

Solutions are given on page 59.

Activity 4.2   Area of a trapezium

(a) What is the area of the region under the graph of the function $f(x) = \frac{2}{3}x + 3$ and above the x-axis, between the lines $x = -3$ and $x = 6$ (see Figure 4.3)?

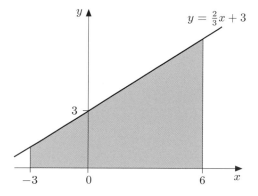

Figure 4.3   A trapezoidal area

(b) Choose an integral F of the function f given in part (a), and evaluate $F(6) - F(-3)$. What do you notice?

Solutions are given on page 59.

On the basis of the results in these two activities, we can surmise that the following might be true.

Hypothesis

Suppose that $f(x)$ is a continuous function that takes no negative values for $a \le x \le b$ (so its graph never goes below the x-axis in the interval $[a, b]$). Then the area bounded by the graph of $y = f(x)$, the x-axis, and the lines $x = a$ and $x = b$, can be evaluated as follows.

(a) Find an integral $F(x)$ of $f(x)$.

(b) Calculate the difference in the values of the function F between a and b, that is, $F(b) - F(a)$.

Note that so far this is just a hypothesis, which is based only on the two simple cases looked at in Activities 4.1 and 4.2. However, it turns out to be correct, and you will see more justification for this claim shortly.

First some new notation and an important definition are introduced. The difference in the values of a function at two points in its domain, as in $F(b) - F(a)$ above, occurs sufficiently frequently in calculus to merit an abbreviated notation. We write

$$F(b) - F(a) = [F(x)]_a^b.$$

> The area described is that shown in Figure 4.1(a).
>
> In fact, if $f(x)$ is a continuous function, then such an $F(x)$ can always be found (though it may not be possible to express its rule as a simple formula). Recall, from the Summary of Block A in Chapter A3, that informally a continuous function is one whose graph can be drawn without lifting pen from paper.
>
> $[F(x)]_a^b$ is pronounced as 'F of x evaluated from a to b'.

Activity 4.3   Evaluating functions from a to b

Evaluate each of the following expressions.

(a) $\left[\frac{1}{2}x^2\right]_3^5$ (b) $[\cos x]_0^{2\pi}$ (c) $[e^x]_{-1}^1$

Solutions are given on page 60.

The hypothesis stated above, for the evaluation of areas, depends on two steps which are not in themselves obviously related to area. These steps are as follows, given any continuous function $f(x)$ and any two values a and b such that the interval $[a, b]$ is in its domain.

(a) Find an integral $F(x)$ of $f(x)$.

(b) Calculate the difference $[F(x)]_a^b = F(b) - F(a)$.

The outcome of these two steps is known as the *definite integral* of the function $f(x)$ from a to b. The value of such a definite integral is the same whichever integral of $f(x)$ is chosen. This is so because if $F(x)$ is one such integral, then any other is equal to $F(x) + c$ for some constant c, and we have

$$[F(x) + c]_a^b = F(b) + c - F(a) - c = [F(x)]_a^b.$$

Thus the value of a definite integral depends on the given function f and on the two numbers a and b, but not on the particular choice of an integral for f.

Consequently, we can denote the definite integral by

$$\int_a^b f(x)\,dx.$$

In this expression, the numbers a and b are called the **limits of integration** with a being the **lower limit** and b the **upper limit**.

Definite integral

The **definite integral** of a continuous function f **from a to b**, denoted by

$$\int_a^b f(x)\,dx,$$

is defined to be

$$[F(x)]_a^b = F(b) - F(a),$$

where F is any integral of f.

Variables other than x can be used in a definite integral *without altering its value*, since that value is simply a number. Thus we have

$$\int_a^b f(x)\,dx = \int_a^b f(t)\,dt = \int_a^b f(u)\,du = \ldots,$$

since all of these expressions equal $F(b) - F(a)$. For this reason, the variable in a definite integral is sometimes called a *dummy variable*.

The definite integral may also be written without an explicit variable of integration, as

$$\int_a^b f,$$

in which case $F(b) - F(a)$ is often written as $[F]_a^b$.

The variable in an *indefinite* integral is not a dummy variable, since it appears also in the resulting family of integrals.

Example 4.1 Evaluating a definite integral

Evaluate the definite integral

$$\int_0^\pi \sin x\,dx.$$

Solution

An integral of $\sin x$ is $-\cos x$. Hence we have

$$\int_0^\pi \sin x\,dx = [-\cos x]_0^\pi$$
$$= -\cos \pi - (-\cos 0)$$
$$= -(-1) - (-1) = 2.$$

Here are some similar problems for you to try.

Activity 4.4 Evaluating definite integrals

Evaluate each of the following definite integrals.

(a) $\displaystyle\int_{-1}^1 x^2\,dx$ (b) $\displaystyle\int_0^2 e^t\,dt$ (c) $\displaystyle\int_1^4 \frac{1}{u}\,du$

Solutions are given on page 60.

Our earlier hypothesis about areas under graphs can now be restated in terms of the definite integral.

A function f for which $f(x) \geq 0$ for all x in an interval $[a, b]$ is said to be *non-negative* on $[a, b]$.

Finding the area under a graph

If $f(x)$ is a continuous function that takes no negative values for $a \leq x \leq b$, then the area of the region bounded by the graph of $y = f(x)$, the x-axis, and the lines $x = a$ and $x = b$, is equal to the definite integral

$$\int_a^b f(x)\, dx.$$

In practice, it is often convenient to abbreviate this phrase to the *area under the graph of $y = f(x)$ from a to b.*

The area described above is referred to as the *area under the graph of $y = f(x)$ from $x = a$ to $x = b$.*

It was claimed earlier that this statement is correct; an explanation follows of why this is so.

Suppose that f is a continuous function that is non-negative on the interval $[a, b]$. Then, for each value of x in the interval, let $A(x)$ denote the area under the graph of $y = f(x)$ from a to x, as shown in Figure 4.4 below. This may be called the *area-so-far function*, where the 'so far' is measured from the starting value a. Thus we have $A(a) = 0$, while $A(b)$ denotes the area under the graph of $y = f(x)$ from a to b.

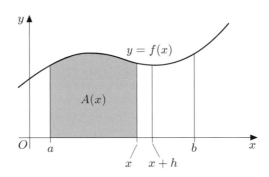

Figure 4.4   Area so far

On this diagram we have also drawn the vertical line through $x + h$, where h is a small positive number. Now consider the region under the graph of $y = f(x)$ from x to $x + h$. On the one hand, the area of this region must equal

$$A(x + h) - A(x),$$

from the definition of the area-so-far function. On the other hand, this region is a strip of width h, and its area is close to that of a rectangle of width h and height $f(x)$, so we can write

$$A(x + h) - A(x) \simeq h f(x). \tag{4.1}$$

Even though (4.1) is not an exact equation, it can be shown that if we divide through by h and take the limit as $h \to 0$, then

$$\lim_{h \to 0}\left(\frac{A(x + h) - A(x)}{h}\right) = f(x).$$

See Chapter C1, Subsection 1.3.

The expression on the left-hand side is the *derivative* of $A(x)$, so

$$A'(x) = f(x).$$

Thus the area-so-far function $A(x)$ satisfies the conditions

$$A'(x) = f(x), \quad A(a) = 0.$$

Now if $F(x)$ is *any* integral of $f(x)$, then the definition of definite integral states that

$$\int_a^b f(x)\,dx = F(b) - F(a).$$

Since $A(x)$ is one such integral, it follows that

$$\int_a^b f(x)\,dx = A(b) - A(a)$$
$$= A(b) \quad \text{(since } A(a) = 0\text{)}.$$

This concludes the argument that the hypothesis stated above is valid. We now put this result to use.

This argument also demonstrates (informally) that an integral of the continuous function f exists, since A is such an integral. It is not hard to extend this conclusion to the case where f may take negative values.

Example 4.2   Finding an area by definite integration

Find the area under the graph of $y = \sin x$ from $x = 0$ to $x = \pi$ (see Figure 4.5).

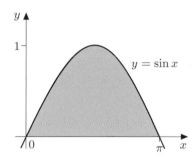

Figure 4.5   Area under the graph

Solution

The area is equal to the definite integral

$$\int_0^\pi \sin x\,dx,$$

whose value was found in Example 4.1 to be 2.

Comment

As a check, note that this region is enclosed within a rectangle of base π and height 1, which has area π, and encloses a triangle of base π and height 1, which has area $\frac{1}{2}\pi$. Thus the area of the region lies between $\frac{1}{2}\pi$ and π, and the calculated answer 2 has this property.

Activity 4.5   Finding areas by definite integration

(a) Find the area under the graph of $y = x^2$ from $x = -1$ to $x = 1$ (see Figure 4.6(a)).

(b) Find the area under the graph of $y = e^{-3t}$ from $t = 0$ to $t = \frac{2}{3}$ (see Figure 4.6(b)), giving your answer to three decimal places.

The Product Rule was introduced in Chapter C1, Subsection 4.1.

(c) (i) Use the Product Rule to show that the derivative of $u(\ln u - 1)$ is $\ln u$.

(ii) Hence find the area under the graph of $y = \ln u$ from $u = 1$ to $u = 2$ (see Figure 4.6(c)), giving your answer to three decimal places.

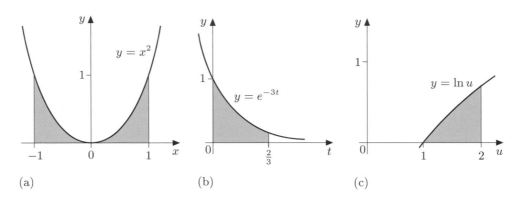

Figure 4.6   Three areas under graphs

Solutions are given on page 60.

Note that definite integrals do not always represent areas. As was said above, if $f(x)$ is a continuous function, for which an integral can be found, and if $f(x) \geq 0$ for all x in the interval $[a, b]$, then the definite integral

$$\int_a^b f(x)\,dx$$

does give the value of the area under the graph of $y = f(x)$ from $x = a$ to $x = b$. However, if we have $f(x) < 0$ for some x in $[a, b]$, then the definite integral above does not represent an area.

For example, you saw in Example 4.2 that the area under the graph of $y = \sin x$ from $x = 0$ to $x = \pi$ is

$$\int_0^\pi \sin x\,dx = 2.$$

On the other hand, we also have

$$\int_\pi^{2\pi} \sin x\,dx = \left[-\cos x\right]_\pi^{2\pi}$$
$$= -\cos(2\pi) - (-\cos \pi)$$
$$= -1 - (-(-1)) = -2.$$

In fact, the definite integral in this case is the *negative* of the area between the graph of $\sin x$ and the x-axis from $x = \pi$ to $x = 2\pi$.

This cannot be the value of an area, since it is negative. A look at the graph of $\sin x$ shows what has happened (see Figure 4.7). This graph is below the x-axis in the interval $(\pi, 2\pi)$, so $\sin x < 0$ in this interval.

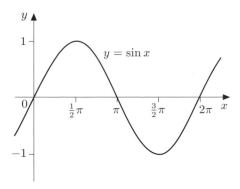

Figure 4.7   Graph of $y = \sin x$

Even when the value of the definite integral is positive, it may not correspond to an area. For example, we obtain

$$\int_0^{3\pi/2} \sin x \, dx = \left[-\cos x\right]_0^{3\pi/2}$$
$$= -\cos(\tfrac{3}{2}\pi) - (-\cos 0)$$
$$= 0 - (-1) = 1$$

but, as Figure 4.7 shows, $\sin x$ takes negative as well as positive values on the interval $[0, \tfrac{3}{2}\pi]$.

In fact, the definite integral here is equal to $A_1 - A_2$, where A_1 is the area *below* the graph of $\sin x$ from $x = 0$ to $x = \pi$ (where $\sin x \geq 0$) and A_2 is the area *above* the graph of $\sin x$ from $x = \pi$ to $x = \tfrac{3}{2}\pi$ (where $\sin x \leq 0$). A similar interpretation of the definite integral in terms of areas above and below the x-axis holds also in other cases.

Activity 4.6   Which are areas?

Which of the following definite integrals

$$\int_a^b f(x) \, dx$$

represents the area under the graph of $y = f(x)$ from $x = a$ to $x = b$?

(a) $\displaystyle\int_{-1}^1 x \, dx$ (b) $\displaystyle\int_{-1}^1 x^2 \, dx$ (c) $\displaystyle\int_0^{3\pi/4} \cos x \, dx$

Solutions are given on page 60.

Finding areas is just one of the many applications of the definite integral. Another is the calculation of change of position, given a velocity function. If a particle moving along a straight line has velocity $v(t)$ at time t, for $a \leq t \leq b$, then the total change of position of the particle between times a and b is given by

$$\int_a^b v(t) \, dt = [s(t)]_a^b = s(b) - s(a),$$

where $s(t)$ is the position function of the particle. This equation is valid without restriction on the sign of $v(t)$, since $s(t)$ has been assigned a meaning whether $v(t)$ is positive, negative or zero.

4.2 Definite integral as a limit of summations

This subsection will not be assessed.

The definite integral method for finding areas under a graph, described in the last subsection, has a potential drawback. It depends on being able to identify an integral $F(x)$ of the original function $f(x)$ under whose graph the area is to be found, but sometimes there is no simple formula which can be found for such an integral. The area must then be sought by alternative means.

In this subsection we investigate an alternative approach to finding the area under a graph. This turns out to have an extra pay-off, in that it leads to an illuminating second view of what the definite integral is.

Designing a sports hall

Imagine that you are an architect who has been commissioned to design a large sports hall. The brief that you were given has led you to specify a rectangular base for the hall, of length 80 m and width 40 m, with a roof which has a uniform cross-section across the width and a central height of 15 m. You decide that this cross-section of the roof should have a pleasing sweep like that shown in Figure 4.8. You choose the function

$$f(x) = 15\sqrt{\sin\left(\frac{\pi x}{40}\right)}$$

to describe the height of this cross-section, since this gives a nearly vertical wall close to floor level.

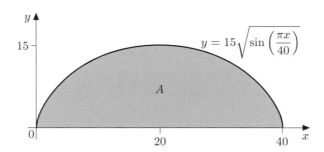

Figure 4.8   Cross-section of sports hall

One of the pieces of information which you are asked to provide is the overall volume of the hall, so that the power supply required to heat the air inside can be determined. This volume is $80A\,\mathrm{m}^3$, where $A\,\mathrm{m}^2$ is the cross-sectional area shown above.

Since the cross-section across the width is uniform, the volume is the length times the cross-sectional area.

You therefore need to calculate A. It can be expressed in terms of a definite integral as

$$A = \int_0^{40} 15\sqrt{\sin\left(\frac{\pi x}{40}\right)}\,dx,$$

but there is no simple formula known for an integral of the function

$$f(x) = 15\sqrt{\sin\left(\frac{\pi x}{40}\right)}.$$

You are therefore forced to consider an alternative approach. Your first thought might be to obtain very rough upper and lower estimates of the area $A\,\mathrm{m}^2$ of the shaded region. It is enclosed within a rectangle of base 40 m and height 15 m, so $A < 600$. It encloses a triangle of the same base and height, so $A > 300$.

One approach to obtaining a closer estimate for A is to approximate the region under the graph by a collection of rectangles, with the estimate being the sum of their areas. A step in this direction is illustrated in Figure 4.9.

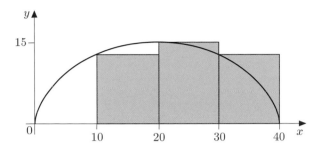

Figure 4.9 Estimating the area with rectangles

The interval $[0, 40]$ has been divided into four equal subintervals, and on each a rectangle has been constructed so that its top *left* corner meets the graph of $f(x)$ (the leftmost 'rectangle' therefore has height zero). The area A is estimated by the sum of the areas of these rectangles, which is

$$10 \times f(0) + 10 \times f(10) + 10 \times f(20) + 10 \times f(30)$$

$$= 10 \left(0 + 15\sqrt{\sin\left(\frac{10\pi}{40}\right)} + 15\sqrt{\sin\left(\frac{20\pi}{40}\right)} + 15\sqrt{\sin\left(\frac{30\pi}{40}\right)} \right)$$

$$= 150 \left(\sqrt{\sin\left(\tfrac{1}{4}\pi\right)} + \sqrt{\sin\left(\tfrac{1}{2}\pi\right)} + \sqrt{\sin\left(\tfrac{3}{4}\pi\right)} \right)$$

$$\simeq 150(0.840\,896 + 1 + 0.840\,896) \simeq 402.27.$$

If you wish to check this calculation, make sure that your calculator is in radian mode.

An improvement to this estimate for A can be found by dividing up the interval $[0, 40]$ into a larger number of subintervals, since the rectangles then approximate more closely the region beneath the graph. With 20 subintervals of width 2, for example, the same construction produces the collection of rectangles shown in Figure 4.10.

Note that this and the further estimates below all lie within the range $300 < A < 600$ which was established with the rough lower and upper estimates.

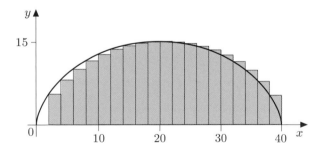

Figure 4.10 Estimating the area using 20 subintervals

The sum of the areas of these rectangles is

$$2 \times f(0) + 2 \times f(2) + 2 \times f(4) + \cdots + 2 \times f(38)$$

$$= 2 \times 15 \left(\sqrt{\sin\left(\frac{2\pi}{40}\right)} + \sqrt{\sin\left(\frac{4\pi}{40}\right)} + \cdots + \sqrt{\sin\left(\frac{38\pi}{40}\right)} \right)$$

$$\simeq 452.71.$$

You are *not* expected to check by hand this and the similar calculations below. The answers were obtained using a computer.

This is the estimate for A based on 20 subintervals. Further improvements can be found by increasing successively the number of subintervals into which the interval $[0, 40]$ is divided. Table 4.1 below shows results obtained in this way.

Table 4.1

Number of subintervals	Sum of areas of rectangles
4	402.27
20	452.71
50	456.41
100	457.21
500	457.62
1 000	457.64
5 000	457.66
10 000	457.66

The numbers in the right-hand column form a sequence that converges in the sense defined in Chapter B1, Subsection 5.1.

The convergence of the values in the right-hand column suggests that we have

$$A = \int_0^{40} 15 \sqrt{\sin\left(\frac{\pi x}{40}\right)}\, dx = 457.66$$

to two decimal places. Thus the volume of the hall is

$$80A = 36\,613\,\mathrm{m}^3.$$

It would usually suffice to quote this answer to three significant figures, as $36\,600\,\mathrm{m}^3$.

Generalising the approach

The calculation of the area A above was achieved without first finding an integral of the given function f whose graph specifies the region of interest. It is possible to generalise this result, and hence to formulate a method of definite integration which relies on computer power rather than on finding a formula for the integral of a function.

Suppose that f is any function which is continuous and non-negative on the interval $[a, b]$. We seek the area under the graph of $y = f(x)$ from $x = a$ to $x = b$, which is the area of the shaded region in Figure 4.11, and is equal to the definite integral

$$\int_a^b f(x)\, dx.$$

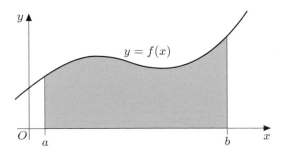

Figure 4.11 Area under the graph

The interval $[a, b]$ is divided into N equal subintervals of width

$$h = \frac{b-a}{N},$$

where N is any positive integer. These N subintervals are

$$[a, a+h], [a+h, a+2h], [a+2h, a+3h], \ldots,$$

with the Nth and final subinterval being

$$[a + (N-1)h, a + Nh] = [b-h, b].$$

Thus the $(i+1)$th subinterval is

$$[a + ih, a + (i+1)h] \quad (i = 0, 1, 2, \ldots, N-1).$$

On each subinterval, we construct a rectangle whose top left corner lies on the graph of $y = f(x)$, as indicated in Figure 4.12.

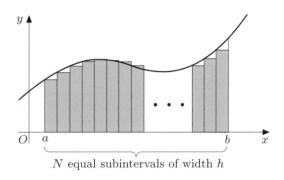

Figure 4.12   Approximating the area with rectangles

For the $(i+1)$th subinterval, the height of the corresponding rectangle is $f(a + ih)$, and its area is

$$hf(a+ih) \quad (i = 0, 1, 2, \ldots, N-1).$$

The sum of the areas of the N rectangles so constructed is

$$\sum_{i=0}^{N-1} hf(a+ih), \quad \text{where } h = \frac{b-a}{N}. \tag{4.1}$$

For each positive integer N, the sum (4.1) gives an approximate estimate of the area

$$\int_a^b f(x)\, dx.$$

Arguing as in the specific case of the sports hall roof considered earlier, the approximation (4.1) becomes closer and closer to the actual value of the area as N increases. Another way of expressing this convergence in the values of the sums is to say that the definite integral is equal to the *limit* of these values as N tends to infinity, which is written as

$$\int_a^b f(x)\, dx = \lim_{N \to \infty} \left[\sum_{i=0}^{N-1} hf(a+ih) \right], \quad \text{where } h = \frac{b-a}{N}. \tag{4.2}$$

Note that we have $h \to 0$ as $N \to \infty$. As N increases, the sum in the square brackets consists of more and more terms, but each individual term makes a smaller and smaller contribution to the whole.

We have deduced equation (4.2) with reference to finding the area under a curve, for which the associated function f was taken to be non-negative on the interval $[a, b]$. However, it turns out that equation (4.2) applies to *any* continuous function f, without restriction on the sign of the values which $f(x)$ takes. This result therefore provides a means of finding the numerical value of any definite integral.

It also provides a more precise description of what is meant by 'area under a graph'.

While we have argued that equation (4.2) is a plausible result, we have not proved its validity, and such a proof is beyond the scope of this course. However, the result is of great importance and usefulness. It carries the name of the *Fundamental Theorem of Calculus*. Indeed, many texts take equation (4.2) as the *definition* of the definite integral. This brings the concept of integration into line with its everyday meaning of 'combining parts into a whole'.

> **Fundamental Theorem of Calculus**
>
> If f is a function which is continuous on the interval $[a, b]$, then
>
> $$\int_a^b f(x)\,dx = \lim_{N \to \infty}\left[\sum_{i=0}^{N-1} h f(a + ih)\right], \quad \text{where } h = \frac{b-a}{N}. \qquad (4.2)$$

It is possible at this point to provide some explanation of where the

$$\int \dots\, dx$$

See Chapter C1, Subsection 3.3.

notation for integrals comes from. Suppose that we replace the subinterval length h by δx ('a small increase in x'), as we did in explaining the Leibniz notation for derivatives. If we also write

$$x_i = a + ih \quad (i = 0, 1, 2, \dots, N-1),$$

then equation (4.2) becomes

You may also see Δx rather than δx in such expressions. Here Δ and δ are the upper- and lower-case versions, respectively, of the Greek letter delta.

$$\int_a^b f(x)\,dx = \lim_{\delta x \to 0}\left[\sum_{i=0}^{N-1} f(x_i)\delta x\right], \quad \text{where } N\delta x = b - a.$$

The elongated S of the integral sign denotes a 'limiting sum', and the dx at the end of the integral is a 'residue' of the δx which appears in each sum on the right-hand side.

Other versions of the summation process described in deriving equation (4.2) lead to a similar outcome. We chose to construct the rectangle on each subinterval so that its height was equal to the function value at the left-hand end of the subinterval. It suffices in fact for the height of this rectangle to equal the function value at *any* point within the subinterval concerned. For example, this point could be taken at the right-hand end of each subinterval, or at its centre. The limit of the sums so created still gives the value of the definite integral.

There have been no activities for you to carry out in this subsection. This is because the results introduced here require the use of a computer for their implementation in practical cases. If you wish, you can see how this is achieved in the next section.

A computer cannot in fact 'take a limit' to evaluate the right-hand side of equation (4.2) in specific cases. However, in practice all that is required is that the sum (4.1) should give the same value, to a specified accuracy, for two large but widely separated values of N (say for one value twice as large as the other). You saw this strategy demonstrated in Table 4.1 on page 48 and in the conclusion drawn from it.

Summary of Section 4

This section has introduced:

◇ the definite integral of a continuous function f from a to b,

$$\int_a^b f(x)\,dx = [F(x)]_a^b = F(b) - F(a),$$

where F is any integral of f;

◇ the fact that if f is a continuous function which takes no negative values for $a \le x \le b$, then the area of the region bounded by the graph of $y = f(x)$, the x-axis, and the lines $x = a$ and $x = b$, is equal to the definite integral

$$\int_a^b f(x)\,dx;$$

◇ the Fundamental Theorem of Calculus.

> You will be expected to find definite integrals 'by hand' for any case where the function to be integrated appears in Table 1.1 on page 15, or is a constant multiple or sum of such functions.

Exercises for Section 4

Exercise 4.1

Evaluate each of the following definite integrals.

(a) $\displaystyle\int_0^{\pi/4} (\cos(5x) + 2\sin(5x))\,dx$ \qquad (b) $\displaystyle\int_1^2 \frac{6}{u^2}\,du$

(c) $\displaystyle\int_0^{\pi} e^t \sin t\,dt$, \quad given that $\frac{1}{2}e^t(\sin t - \cos t)$ is an integral of $e^t \sin t$.

Exercise 4.2

(a) Find the area under the graph of $y = 2x^3$ from $x = 1$ to $x = 2$.

(b) Show that $x(3 - x) > 0$ when $0 < x < 3$. Hence find the area which is bounded by the graph of $y = x(3 - x)$ and by the x-axis.

(c) Using the fact that $\arctan x$ is an integral of $1/(1 + x^2)$, find the area under the graph of $y = 1/(1 + x^2)$ from $x = -2$ to $x = 2$.

Exercise 4.3

This exercise asks you to derive the standard formula for the area enclosed within a circle of radius R. Suppose that $A(r)$ denotes the area within a circle with radius $r \le R$.

(a) What is the value of $A(0)$?

(b) Write down an expression, in terms of the function A, for the area of the annulus shown shaded in Figure 4.13, which has inner radius r and outer radius $r + h$.

(c) Write down another (approximate) expression for the area of this annulus, noting that it has width h and inner circumference $2\pi r$ (the latter follows from the definition of π as the ratio of circumference to diameter for any circle).

(d) Write down the approximate relationship between the two expressions found in parts (b) and (c). By dividing this relationship through by h and then taking the limit as $h \to 0$, show that $A'(r) = 2\pi r$.

(e) By integrating both sides of the equation $A'(r) = 2\pi r$ and then using the result of part (a), deduce that $A(R) = \pi R^2$.

> The argument required here is similar to that using the area-so-far function in Subsection 4.1.

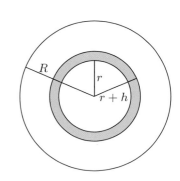

Figure 4.13 Annulus

5 Integration with the computer

 To study this section, you will need access to your computer, together with Computer Book C.

In Sections 1 and 2 you saw how to find the indefinite integrals of a wide range of functions. Section 4 showed how a definite integral can be evaluated once the corresponding indefinite integral has been found.

Both indefinite and definite integrals can in principle be found using a computer algebra system. As with differentiation, you are expected to be able to find the integrals of simpler functions 'by hand', using the table, rules and methods in this text. It should only be for more complicated cases that the computer needs to be used, and in such cases it provides a powerful tool.

Refer to Computer Book C for the work in this section.

In your work during this section you should have gained confidence in using your computer for integration, while noting certain respects in which care must be taken with the results.

The skill involved in using the computer for more complicated integrals is largely confined to typing in correctly the algebraic expressions to be integrated, though it is useful to remember that each answer can be checked by applying the derivative operator to the outcome of an integral, to see whether this produces the original function.

Apart from undertaking such checks, you are taking on trust that the computer algebra system 'knows what it is doing'. This raises two important questions.

◇ How are the answers obtained?

◇ How can we be sure (other than by constant checking, and that may involve another computer operation) that the answers are always correct?

These questions are beyond the scope of MST121, but you can expect to see them considered if you take your mathematical studies further. This will entail, among other things, an extension to your ability to integrate 'by hand'.

Summary of Section 5

This section has used the computer to find a variety of indefinite and definite integrals.

Summary of Chapter C2

In this chapter you saw integration defined as the reverse process of differentiation, and undertook much practice in finding indefinite integrals for various functions. You also saw how integration can be applied to find areas under the graphs of functions, using definite integrals.

Learning outcomes

You have been working towards the following learning outcomes.

Terms to know and use

Integration, an integral, the indefinite integral, arbitrary constant, constant of integration, integral sign, integrand, double-angle formulas, kinematics, position, distance, velocity, speed, acceleration, SI units, area under a graph, definite integral, limits of integration, upper/lower limit, non-negative function, dummy variable, area-so-far function.

Symbols and notation to know and use

$\diamond$ $\displaystyle\int f(x)\,dx$ (indefinite integral);

$\diamond$ $[F(x)]_a^b$ (function evaluated from a to b);

$\diamond$ $\displaystyle\int_a^b f(x)\,dx$ or $\displaystyle\int_a^b f$ (definite integral).

Mathematical skills

$\diamond$ Integrate 'by hand' any function of a type shown in Table 1.1 on page 15. Also, integrate any constant multiple, a sum or difference, and a sum of constant multiples of those same functions. This applies to finding both indefinite and definite integrals.

$\diamond$ Integrate by inspection, where appropriate.

$\diamond$ Evaluate a definite integral, where an integral is known or can be found.

$\diamond$ Use integration to find an area under the graph of a function.

Mathcad skills

$\diamond$ Type expressions to be integrated (or otherwise manipulated) directly into Mathcad, without the use of a prepared file.

$\diamond$ Apply Mathcad to integrate an expression symbolically.

$\diamond$ Remember that what Mathcad outputs as an 'indefinite integral' is an integral without an arbitrary constant.

$\diamond$ Apply Mathcad to find a definite integral symbolically.

$\diamond$ Apply Mathcad to find a definite integral numerically.

Modelling skills

$\diamond$ Use the model of constant acceleration for a particle in one-dimensional motion, where appropriate.

Ideas to be aware of

◇   That *the indefinite* integral is a family of functions, *an* integral is a single function and a *definite* integral is a number.

◇   That integration is both an 'undoing' of differentiation and a limit of a sequence of sums, with these two interpretations being linked by the Fundamental Theorem of Calculus.

◇   That definite integrals represent areas under graphs where the integrand is non-negative.

◇   That for one-dimensional motion of a particle with constant acceleration, the position and velocity of the particle can be related directly to each other.

Appendix: Double-angle formulas

This appendix shows that

$$\sin(2\theta) = 2\sin\theta\cos\theta, \quad \cos(2\theta) = \cos^2\theta - \sin^2\theta. \tag{A.1}$$

It can be established that both sides of both equations are functions with period π, so it suffices to show that the results hold for $0 \le \theta < \pi$. We do this in three stages for the first equation: (i) for $\theta = 0$ and $\theta = \frac{1}{2}\pi$, (ii) for $0 < \theta < \frac{1}{2}\pi$, (iii) for $\frac{1}{2}\pi < \theta < \pi$.

(i) By direct evaluation, the first formula holds for $\theta = 0$ and $\theta = \frac{1}{2}\pi$.

(ii) Suppose next that $0 < \theta < \frac{1}{2}\pi$. Then right-angled triangles ABD, ACD can be drawn as shown in Figure A.1, with $\angle BAD = \angle CAD = \theta$, $AB = AC = 1$, $BD = DC = \sin\theta$ and $AD = \cos\theta$. The area of $\triangle ABC$ is

◇ $\frac{1}{2} \times AB \times AC \times \sin(\angle BAC) = \frac{1}{2}\sin(2\theta)$, using '$\frac{1}{2}bc\sin A$';

◇ $\frac{1}{2} \times BC \times AD = \sin\theta\cos\theta$, using '$\frac{1}{2}$ base $\times$ height'.

It follows from the equality of these expressions that

$$\sin(2\theta) = 2\sin\theta\cos\theta, \quad \text{for } 0 < \theta < \tfrac{1}{2}\pi. \tag{A.2}$$

(iii) Suppose now that $\frac{1}{2}\pi < \theta < \pi$. Then the angle $\phi = \pi - \theta$ lies in the range $0 < \phi < \frac{1}{2}\pi$, so satisfying equation (A.2); that is,

$$\sin(2\phi) = 2\sin\phi\cos\phi.$$

Hence, using standard trigonometric identities, we have

$$\begin{aligned}
\sin(2\theta) &= \sin(2\pi - 2\phi) \\
&= \sin(-2\phi) \\
&= -\sin(2\phi) \\
&= -2\sin\phi\cos\phi \\
&= 2\sin(\pi - \phi)\cos(\pi - \phi) \\
&= 2\sin\theta\cos\theta, \quad \text{for } \tfrac{1}{2}\pi < \theta < \pi.
\end{aligned}$$

Thus we have established the first of equations (A.1) for all values of θ.

The second of equations (A.1) could be shown in a similar way, using the Cosine Rule for $0 < \theta < \frac{1}{2}\pi$. However, it is also obtained by differentiating the first equation! The Product Rule is needed to differentiate the right-hand side of this equation.

The material in this appendix will not be assessed.

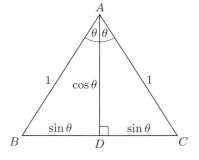

Figure A.1   Triangles

Solutions to Activities

Solution 1.1

In each case, the result of differentiating the given position function is

$$\frac{ds}{dt} = 6t.$$

Solution 1.2

In each solution, c is an arbitrary constant.

(a) $\int \left(\frac{1}{x} + e^{3x} \right) dx = \ln x + \frac{1}{3}e^{3x} + c$

(b) $\int \left(3\sqrt{x} + \frac{8}{\sqrt{x}} \right) dx = \int \left(3x^{1/2} + 8x^{-1/2} \right) dx$

$$= 3\left(\frac{2}{3}x^{3/2}\right) + 8\left(2x^{1/2}\right) + c$$
$$= 2x^{3/2} + 16x^{1/2} + c$$

(c) $\int (a\sin(\omega t) + b\cos(\omega t))\, dt$

$$= -\frac{a}{\omega}\cos(\omega t) + \frac{b}{\omega}\sin(\omega t) + c$$

(d) $\int \left(\frac{2}{3}x^{5/3} - 5x^{-3/2} + 4e^{-2x} \right) dx$

$$= \frac{2}{3}\left(\frac{3}{8}x^{8/3}\right) - 5\left(-2x^{-1/2}\right) + 4\left(-\frac{1}{2}e^{-2x}\right) + c$$
$$= \frac{1}{4}x^{8/3} + 10x^{-1/2} - 2e^{-2x} + c$$

Solution 1.3

In each solution, c is an arbitrary constant.

(a) $\int \frac{1}{2}(e^x + e^{-x})\, dx = \frac{1}{2}(e^x - e^{-x}) + c$

(b) $\int \frac{1}{2}(e^x - e^{-x})\, dx = \frac{1}{2}(e^x + e^{-x}) + c$

Solution 2.1

In each solution, c is an arbitrary constant.

(a) $\int (x+1)^2\, dx = \int (x^2 + 2x + 1)\, dx$

$$= \frac{1}{3}x^3 + x^2 + x + c$$

(b) $\int \frac{x^2 + 1}{x^4}\, dx = \int (x^{-2} + x^{-4})\, dx$

$$= -x^{-1} - \frac{1}{3}x^{-3} + c$$
$$= -\frac{1}{x} - \frac{1}{3x^3} + c$$

(c) $\int \sqrt[3]{x} \left(10x^2 - \frac{1}{x^2} \right) dx$

$$= \int x^{1/3}(10x^2 - x^{-2})\, dx$$
$$= \int (10x^{7/3} - x^{-5/3})\, dx$$
$$= 10\left(\frac{3}{10}x^{10/3}\right) - \left(-\frac{3}{2}x^{-2/3}\right) + c$$
$$= 3x^{10/3} + \frac{3}{2}x^{-2/3} + c$$

Solution 2.2

In each solution, c is an arbitrary constant.

(a) $\int e^{2x-1}\, dx = \int e^{2x}e^{-1}\, dx$

$$= \int e^{-1}e^{2x}\, dx$$
$$= \frac{1}{2}e^{-1}e^{2x} + c$$
$$= \frac{1}{2}e^{2x-1} + c$$

(b) $\int (2 + e^{x/2})(1 - e^{-x/2})\, dx$

$$= \int \left(2 - 2e^{-x/2} + e^{x/2} - e^{x/2}e^{-x/2} \right) dx$$
$$= \int \left(2 - 2e^{-x/2} + e^{x/2} - 1 \right) dx$$
$$= \int \left(1 - 2e^{-x/2} + e^{x/2} \right) dx$$
$$= x + 4e^{-x/2} + 2e^{x/2} + c$$

Solution 2.3

(a) From the third version of the double-angle formula for $\cos(2\theta)$, with $\theta = x$, we have

$$\cos(2x) = 1 - 2\sin^2 x,$$

which can be rearranged to give

$$\sin^2 x = \frac{1}{2}(1 - \cos(2x)).$$

Hence the required indefinite integral is

$$\int \sin^2 x\, dx = \int \left(\frac{1}{2} - \frac{1}{2}\cos(2x)\right) dx$$
$$= \frac{1}{2}x - \frac{1}{4}\sin(2x) + c,$$

where c is an arbitrary constant.

(This answer can also be expressed as $\frac{1}{2}x - \frac{1}{2}\sin x \cos x + c$.)

(b) From the double-angle formula for $\sin(2\theta)$, with $\theta = x$, we have

$$\sin^2 x \cos^2 x = (\sin x \cos x)^2 = \frac{1}{4}\sin^2(2x).$$

The double-angle formula for $\cos(2\theta)$, with $\theta = 2x$, can be written as

$$\cos(4x) = 1 - 2\sin^2(2x),$$

which gives

$$\sin^2(2x) = \tfrac{1}{2}(1 - \cos(4x)).$$

Thus we have

$$\sin^2 x \cos^2 x = \tfrac{1}{4}\sin^2(2x) = \tfrac{1}{8}(1 - \cos(4x)).$$

Hence the required indefinite integral is

$$\int \sin^2 x \cos^2 x \, dx = \int (\tfrac{1}{8} - \tfrac{1}{8}\cos(4x)) \, dx$$
$$= \tfrac{1}{8}x - \tfrac{1}{32}\sin(4x) + c,$$

where c is an arbitrary constant.

Solution 2.4

(a) Noting that $y = \tan x = \sin x/(\cos x)$, and applying the Quotient Rule, we have

$$\frac{dy}{dx} = \frac{1}{\cos^2 x} \left(\cos x \frac{d}{dx}(\sin x) - \sin x \frac{d}{dx}(\cos x) \right)$$
$$= \sec^2 x(\cos x(\cos x) - \sin x(-\sin x))$$
$$= \sec^2 x(\cos^2 x + \sin^2 x) = \sec^2 x.$$

(b) It follows from part (a) that

$$\int \sec^2 x \, dx = \tan x + c,$$

where c is an arbitrary constant.

(c) It follows from equation (2.2) that

$$\tan^2 x = \sec^2 x - 1.$$

Using also the result of part (b), we therefore have

$$\int \tan^2 x \, dx = \int (\sec^2 x - 1) \, dx$$
$$= \tan x - x + c,$$

where c is an arbitrary constant.

Solution 2.5

(a) (i) We need to differentiate $y = u^5$, where $u = x^3 + 1$. Applying the Composite Rule, we have

$$\frac{dy}{dx} = \frac{dy}{du}\frac{du}{dx}$$
$$= \frac{d}{du}(u^5)\frac{d}{dx}(x^3 + 1)$$
$$= 5u^4 \times 3x^2 = 15x^2(x^3 + 1)^4.$$

(ii) We need to differentiate $y = u^3$, where $u = \sin x$. Applying the Composite Rule, we have

$$\frac{dy}{dx} = \frac{dy}{du}\frac{du}{dx}$$
$$= \frac{d}{du}(u^3)\frac{d}{dx}(\sin x)$$
$$= 3u^2 \cos x = 3\sin^2 x \cos x.$$

(iii) We need to differentiate $y = \ln u$, where $u = x^2 + 1$. Applying the Composite Rule, we have

$$\frac{dy}{dx} = \frac{dy}{du}\frac{du}{dx}$$
$$= \frac{d}{du}(\ln u)\frac{d}{dx}(x^2 + 1)$$
$$= \frac{1}{u} \times 2x = \frac{2x}{x^2 + 1}.$$

(b) (i) From part (a)(i), we obtain

$$\int x^2(x^3 + 1)^4 \, dx = \tfrac{1}{15}(x^3 + 1)^5 + c,$$

where c is an arbitrary constant.

(ii) Similarly, from part (a)(ii), we find that

$$\int \sin^2 x \cos x \, dx = \tfrac{1}{3}\sin^3 x + c,$$

where c is an arbitrary constant.

(iii) From part (a)(iii), we obtain

$$\int \frac{x}{x^2 + 1} \, dx = \tfrac{1}{2}\ln(x^2 + 1) + c,$$

where c is an arbitrary constant.

Solution 2.6

(a) In the integrand $x^2(8 - x^3)^5$, the factor x^2 is, except for a constant multiple, the derivative of $8 - x^3$. Hence we can apply equation (2.3) with $f(x) = 8 - x^3$ and $n = 5$. Since $f'(x) = -3x^2$, we write $x^2 = -\tfrac{1}{3}(-3x^2)$ before applying the formula. Thus we have

$$\int x^2(8 - x^3)^5 \, dx = -\tfrac{1}{3}\int (8 - x^3)^5(-3x^2) \, dx$$
$$= -\tfrac{1}{3} \times \tfrac{1}{6}(8 - x^3)^6 + c$$
$$= -\tfrac{1}{18}(8 - x^3)^6 + c,$$

where c is an arbitrary constant.

(b) The integrand is $x^2/(x^3 - 8)$. Here the numerator x^2 is, except for a constant multiple, the derivative of the denominator $x^3 - 8$. So we can apply equation (2.4) with $f(x) = x^3 - 8$. Since $f'(x) = 3x^2$, we write the numerator as $x^2 = \tfrac{1}{3}(3x^2)$ before applying the formula. Thus we have

$$\int \frac{x^2}{x^3 - 8} \, dx = \tfrac{1}{3}\int \frac{3x^2}{x^3 - 8} \, dx$$
$$= \tfrac{1}{3}\ln(x^3 - 8) + c,$$

where c is an arbitrary constant.

(c) The integrand is $\tan x = \sin x/(\cos x)$. Here the numerator $\sin x$ is, except for a constant multiple, the derivative of the denominator $\cos x$, so we can apply equation (2.4) with $f(x) = \cos x$.

Since $f'(x) = -\sin x$, we write the numerator as $\sin x = -(-\sin x)$ before applying the formula. Thus we have

$$\int \tan x \, dx = -\int \frac{(-\sin x)}{\cos x} dx$$
$$= -\ln(\cos x) + c,$$

where c is an arbitrary constant.

(d) The integrand $(2x+5)^7$ is of the form $(f(x))^7$, where $f'(x) = 2$ is a constant. Hence we can apply equation (2.3) with $f(x) = 2x + 5$ and $n = 7$, after adjusting for the factor $f'(x) = 2$. Thus we have

$$\int (2x+5)^7 \, dx = \frac{1}{2} \int (2x+5)^7 (2) \, dx$$
$$= \frac{1}{2} \times \frac{1}{8}(2x+5)^8 + c$$
$$= \frac{1}{16}(2x+5)^8 + c,$$

where c is an arbitrary constant.

Solution 2.7

(a) (i) From equation (2.1) we obtain the trigonometric identity $\sin^2 x = 1 - \cos^2 x$, so that

$$\sin^3 x = \sin^2 x \sin x$$
$$= (1 - \cos^2 x)\sin x$$
$$= \sin x - \cos^2 x \sin x,$$

as required.

(ii) Hence

$$\int \sin^3 x \, dx = \int (\sin x - \cos^2 x \sin x) \, dx$$
$$= \int \sin x \, dx - \int \cos^2 x \sin x \, dx$$
$$= -\cos x - \int \cos^2 x \sin x \, dx.$$

The remaining integral can be found by applying equation (2.3) with $f(x) = \cos x$ and $n = 2$ (recalling that $\cos^2 x = (\cos x)^2$). Since $f'(x) = -\sin x$, we write $\sin x = -(-\sin x)$ before applying the formula. Thus we have

$$-\int \cos^2 x \sin x \, dx = \int \cos^2 x (-\sin x) \, dx$$
$$= \frac{1}{3} \cos^3 x + c,$$

where c is an arbitrary constant. It follows that

$$\int \sin^3 x \, dx = -\cos x + \frac{1}{3} \cos^3 x + c.$$

(b) Carrying out the specified multiplications by x, we have

$$\int \frac{x}{x^2 - 1/x} dx = \int \frac{x^2}{x^3 - 1} dx.$$

On the right-hand side, the numerator x^2 of the integrand is, except for a constant multiple, the derivative of the denominator $x^3 - 1$, so we can apply equation (2.4) with $f(x) = x^3 - 1$. Since $f'(x) = 3x^2$, we write the numerator as

$x^2 = \frac{1}{3}(3x^2)$ before applying the formula. Thus we have

$$\int \frac{x}{x^2 - 1/x} dx = \frac{1}{3} \int \frac{3x^2}{x^3 - 1} dx$$
$$= \frac{1}{3} \ln(x^3 - 1) + c,$$

where c is an arbitrary constant.

Solution 3.1

(a) We have

$$\frac{dv}{dt} = a = 10 \quad (t > 0) \quad \text{and} \quad v = 0 \text{ when } t = 0.$$

Hence integration gives

$$v = \int 10 \, dt = 10t + c,$$

where c is an arbitrary constant. Putting $v = 0$ and $t = 0$ into this equation, we find that $0 = 10 \times 0 + c$, so $c = 0$. Hence we have the velocity function

$$v = 10t \quad (t > 0).$$

(b) On integrating

$$\frac{ds}{dt} = v = 10t \quad (t > 0),$$

we obtain

$$s = 10(\tfrac{1}{2}t^2) + c = 5t^2 + c,$$

where c is an arbitrary constant. However, due to the stated choice of origin, we have $s = 0$ when $t = 0$, so that $0 = 5 \times 0 + c$; that is, $c = 0$. We conclude that the position function is

$$s = 5t^2 \quad (t > 0).$$

(c) The bungee is 30 metres long when unstretched, so it starts to stretch when

$$s = 5t^2 = 30, \quad \text{that is,} \quad t^2 = 6.$$

The solution $t = -\sqrt{6}$ can be rejected as unrealistic within the model, which leaves the solution $t = \sqrt{6}$. Hence the bungee starts to stretch after $\sqrt{6} \simeq 2.45$ seconds.

At this time, the corresponding velocity is obtained from the result of part (a). When $t = \sqrt{6}$, we have

$$v = 10t = 10\sqrt{6} \simeq 24.5.$$

Hence the speed of the person reaches $24.5 \, \text{m s}^{-1}$ at the moment when the bungee starts to stretch.

Solution 3.2

The two given equations are

$$v = at + v_0,$$
$$s = \tfrac{1}{2}at^2 + v_0 t + s_0.$$

On solving the first equation for t, we have

$$t = \frac{v - v_0}{a}.$$

Using this to substitute for t in the second equation gives

$$s = \tfrac{1}{2}a\left(\frac{v - v_0}{a}\right)^2 + v_0\left(\frac{v - v_0}{a}\right) + s_0.$$

After multiplying both sides by $2a$, we obtain

$$2as = (v - v_0)^2 + 2v_0(v - v_0) + 2as_0$$
$$= v^2 - v_0^2 + 2as_0,$$

which may also be written as

$$v^2 - 2as = v_0^2 - 2as_0.$$

Solution 3.3

(a) Assume that the aircraft (modelled as a particle) moves in a straight line. Equation (3.6) is

$$v^2 - 2as = v_0^2 - 2as_0.$$

Choosing the s-axis to point in the direction of motion of the aircraft, with the origin at its point of touch-down, we have $s_0 = 0$ and $v_0 = 70$, giving

$$v^2 - 2as = 70^2.$$

For the minimum deceleration, we need $v = 5$ when $s = 550$. On putting these values into the equation above and solving for a, we obtain

$$a = \frac{5^2 - 70^2}{2 \times 550} = \frac{-4875}{1100} = -\frac{195}{44} \simeq -4.43.$$

The minimum required magnitude of acceleration (deceleration) is therefore $4.43\,\mathrm{m\,s^{-2}}$.

(b) The corresponding time of travel along the runway can be obtained from equation (3.1). Taking $t = 0$ at the moment of touch-down, we have

$$t = \frac{v - v_0}{a}$$
$$= -\frac{44(5 - 70)}{195} = \frac{44}{3} \simeq 14.7 \text{ (in s)}.$$

Hence the aircraft takes $14.7\,\mathrm{s}$ to travel the length of the runway.

Solution 4.1

(a) The area required is that of a rectangle, with base 5 and height 3, so its area is $3 \times 5 = 15$.

(b) Since $f(x) = 3$ is a constant function, an integral is

$$F(x) = 3x.$$

(Any choice of the form $F(x) = 3x + c$, where c is a constant, is correct here, but $F(x) = 3x$ is the simplest choice.) Then we have

$$F(5) - F(0) = 15 - 0 = 15,$$

which is the same value as the value for the area calculated in part (a).

Solution 4.2

(a) The area required is that of a trapezium, which may be regarded as the sum of a rectangle, with base $6 - (-3) = 9$ and height $f(-3) = 1$, and a triangle with the same base and with height $f(6) - f(-3) = 7 - 1 = 6$; see Figure S.1. The area is therefore

$$9 \times 1 + \tfrac{1}{2} \times 9 \times 6 = 36.$$

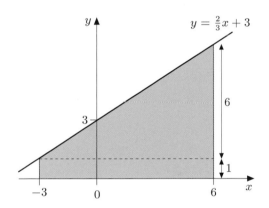

Figure S.1

(Alternatively, the area of any trapezium can be found by applying the rule 'half the sum of the lengths of the parallel sides times the (perpendicular) distance between them'.)

(b) An integral of $f(x) = \tfrac{2}{3}x + 3$ is

$$F(x) = \tfrac{1}{3}x^2 + 3x.$$

(Any choice of the form $F(x) = \tfrac{1}{3}x^2 + 3x + c$, where c is a constant, is correct here.) Then we have

$$F(6) - F(-3)$$
$$= \left(\tfrac{1}{3}(6)^2 + 3 \times 6\right) - \left(\tfrac{1}{3}(-3)^2 + 3 \times (-3)\right) = 36,$$

which is the same value as the value for the area calculated in part (a).

Solution 4.3

(a) $[\frac{1}{2}x^2]_3^5 = \frac{1}{2} \times 5^2 - \frac{1}{2} \times 3^2 = \frac{1}{2}(25 - 9) = 8.$

(b) $[\cos x]_0^{2\pi} = \cos(2\pi) - \cos 0 = 1 - 1 = 0.$

(c) $[e^x]_{-1}^1 = e^1 - e^{-1} = e - e^{-1} \simeq 2.35.$

Solution 4.4

(a) An integral of x^2 is $\frac{1}{3}x^3$, so we have

$$\int_{-1}^1 x^2 \, dx = [\tfrac{1}{3}x^3]_{-1}^1$$
$$= \tfrac{1}{3} \times 1^3 - \tfrac{1}{3} \times (-1)^3 = \tfrac{2}{3}.$$

(b) An integral of e^t is e^t, so we have

$$\int_0^2 e^t \, dt = [e^t]_0^2$$
$$= e^2 - e^0 = e^2 - 1 \simeq 6.39.$$

(c) An integral of $1/u$ is $\ln u$ (for $u > 0$), so we have

$$\int_1^4 \frac{1}{u} \, du = [\ln u]_1^4$$
$$= \ln 4 - \ln 1 = \ln 4 \simeq 1.39.$$

Solution 4.5

(a) The area required is

$$\int_{-1}^1 x^2 \, dx,$$

whose value you found in Activity 4.4(a) to be $\frac{2}{3}$.

(b) The area required is

$$\int_0^{2/3} e^{-3t} \, dt = [-\tfrac{1}{3}e^{-3t}]_0^{2/3}$$
$$= -\tfrac{1}{3}e^{-2} - (-\tfrac{1}{3}e^0)$$
$$= \tfrac{1}{3}(1 - e^{-2}) \simeq 0.288.$$

(c) (i) Using the Product Rule, we have

$$\frac{d}{du}(u(\ln u - 1))$$
$$= \frac{d}{du}(u)(\ln u - 1) + u\frac{d}{du}(\ln u - 1)$$
$$= (1)(\ln u - 1) + u\left(\frac{1}{u}\right)$$
$$= \ln u - 1 + 1 = \ln u.$$

(ii) From the result of part (i), an integral of $\ln u$ is $u(\ln u - 1)$. Hence the area required is

$$\int_1^2 \ln u \, du = [u(\ln u - 1)]_1^2$$
$$= 2(\ln 2 - 1) - 1(\ln 1 - 1)$$
$$= 2\ln 2 - 1 \simeq 0.386.$$

Solution 4.6

(a) The function $f(x) = x$ takes negative values for $x < 0$, so is negative on part of the interval $[-1, 1]$. Thus the integral

$$\int_{-1}^1 x \, dx$$

does not represent an area.

(b) The function $f(x) = x^2$ is zero at $x = 0$, but is otherwise positive. Hence the integral

$$\int_{-1}^1 x^2 \, dx$$

represents the area under the graph of x^2 from -1 to 1. (In fact, you found this area in Activity 4.5(a).)

(c) The function $f(x) = \cos x$ is negative for $\pi/2 < x \le 3\pi/4$. Thus the integral

$$\int_0^{3\pi/4} \cos x \, dx$$

does not represent an area.

Solutions to Exercises

Solution 1.1

In each solution, c is an arbitrary constant.

(a) $\displaystyle\int t^\pi \, dt = \frac{t^{\pi+1}}{\pi+1} + c$

(b) $\displaystyle\int \left(\frac{3}{y^4} + 5\sin(5y) \right) dy = \int (3y^{-4} + 5\sin(5y)) \, dy$

$\displaystyle = -y^{-3} - \cos(5y) + c$

(c) $\displaystyle\int 2\cos\left(\frac{s}{7}\right) ds = 14\sin\left(\frac{s}{7}\right) + c$

(d) $\displaystyle\int \left(\frac{3}{v} + e^{4v} \right) dv = 3\ln v + \tfrac{1}{4}e^{4v} + c$

(e) $\displaystyle\int \tfrac{1}{2}e^{x/4} \, dx = 2e^{x/4} + c$

Solution 2.1

In each solution, c is an arbitrary constant.

(a) $\displaystyle\int t\sqrt{t} \, dt = \int t^{3/2} \, dt$

$\displaystyle = \tfrac{2}{5}t^{5/2} + c$

(b) $\displaystyle\int e^{1+3x} \, dx = \int e^1 e^{3x} \, dx$

$\displaystyle = \tfrac{1}{3}e^1 e^{3x} + c = \tfrac{1}{3}e^{1+3x} + c$

(c) $\displaystyle\int x\left(x^3 + 2x^{-2/3} - \frac{1}{x} \right) dx = \int (x^4 + 2x^{1/3} - 1) \, dx$

$\displaystyle = \tfrac{1}{5}x^5 + \tfrac{3}{2}x^{4/3} - x + c$

(d) Here we use a double-angle formula for $\cos(2\theta)$, with $\theta = 4u$, which gives

$$\cos^2(4u) = \tfrac{1}{2}(\cos(8u) + 1).$$

The required indefinite integral is

$$\int \cos^2(4u) \, du = \int (\tfrac{1}{2}\cos(8u) + \tfrac{1}{2}) \, du$$

$$= \tfrac{1}{16}\sin(8u) + \tfrac{1}{2}u + c.$$

Solution 2.2

(a) The factor $\sin x$ in the integrand is, except for a constant multiple, the derivative of $\cos x$, so we can apply equation (2.3) with $f(x) = \cos x$ and $n = 3$. Since $f'(x) = -\sin x$, we write $\sin x = -(-\sin x)$ before applying the formula. Thus we have

$$\int \sin x \cos^3 x \, dx = -\int \cos^3 x (-\sin x) \, dx$$

$$= -\tfrac{1}{4}\cos^4 x + c,$$

where c is an arbitrary constant.

(b) The integrand can be written as $x^2(x^3 + 1)^{-2}$. The factor x^2 is, except for a constant multiple,

the derivative of $x^3 + 1$, so we can apply equation (2.3) with $f(x) = x^3 + 1$ and $n = -2$. Since $f'(x) = 3x^2$, we write $x^2 = \tfrac{1}{3}(3x^2)$ before applying the formula. Thus we have

$$\int \frac{x^2}{(x^3+1)^2} \, dx = \tfrac{1}{3}\int (x^3+1)^{-2}(3x^2) \, dx$$

$$= \tfrac{1}{3} \times (-1) \times (x^3+1)^{-1} + c$$

$$= -\frac{1}{3(x^3+1)} + c,$$

where c is an arbitrary constant.

Solution 2.3

(a) On multiplying top and bottom of the fraction in the integrand by e^{-x}, we obtain

$$\int \frac{e^{2x} - 1}{e^{2x} + 1} \, dx = \int \frac{e^x - e^{-x}}{e^x + e^{-x}} \, dx.$$

On the right-hand side, the numerator of the integrand is the derivative of the denominator, so we may apply equation (2.4) with $f(x) = e^x + e^{-x}$. This gives

$$\int \frac{e^{2x} - 1}{e^{2x} + 1} \, dx = \ln(e^x + e^{-x}) + c,$$

where c is an arbitrary constant.

(b) Starting from the given right-hand side, we have

$$1 - \frac{2}{e^{2x} + 1} = \frac{e^{2x} + 1}{e^{2x} + 1} - \frac{2}{e^{2x} + 1}$$

$$= \frac{e^{2x} + 1 - 2}{e^{2x} + 1}$$

$$= \frac{e^{2x} - 1}{e^{2x} + 1}.$$

Hence, using the result of part (a), we obtain

$$\int \frac{1}{e^{2x} + 1} \, dx = \tfrac{1}{2}\int \left(1 - \frac{e^{2x} - 1}{e^{2x} + 1} \right) dx$$

$$= \tfrac{1}{2}(x - \ln(e^x + e^{-x})) + c,$$

where c is an arbitrary constant.

(c) On dividing top and bottom of the fraction in the integrand by x, we obtain

$$\int \frac{1}{x\ln x} \, dx = \int \frac{1/x}{\ln x} \, dx.$$

On the right-hand side, the numerator of the integrand is the derivative of the denominator, so we may apply equation (2.4) with $f(x) = \ln x$. This gives

$$\int \frac{1}{x\ln x} \, dx = \ln(\ln x) + c,$$

where c is an arbitrary constant.

Solution 3.1

(a) Choose the s-axis to point vertically upwards, with origin at the point of projection of the ball. Then the ball (modelled as a particle) has constant acceleration $-g$.

The ball attains its maximum height when its velocity is zero. The most direct approach to finding this height is to apply equation (3.6). We have

$$v^2 - 2as = v_0^2 - 2as_0,$$

where $a = -g \simeq -10$, $s_0 = 0$ and $v_0 = 25$. Thus when $v = 0$, we obtain

$$s = -\frac{v_0^2}{2a} = \frac{25^2}{2 \times 10} = 31.25,$$

so the maximum height reached by the ball is 31.25 metres above its point of projection.

(b) The ball returns to its point of projection when $s = 0$ for the second time. According to equation (3.2), we have

$$s = \tfrac{1}{2}at^2 + v_0t + s_0,$$

but with $a = -10$, $v_0 = 25$ and $s_0 = 0$, this becomes

$$s = 25t - 5t^2 = 5t(5 - t).$$

Thus $s = 0$ either at $t = 0$ (which is when the ball is projected) or at $t = 5$, so the ball returns to the point of projection after 5 seconds.

(c) The ball is 20 metres above its point of projection when $s = 20$, that is, when

$$20 = 25t - 5t^2, \quad \text{or} \quad 5t^2 - 25t + 20 = 0.$$

This quadratic equation factorises as

$$5(t - 1)(t - 4) = 0,$$

which has solutions $t = 1$ and $t = 4$. Therefore the ball is 20 m above its point of projection at 1 s and 4 s after it has been projected.

Solution 3.2

(a) We need to differentiate $y = \cos u$, where $u = 2t - \theta$. Applying the Composite Rule, we have

$$\frac{dy}{dt} = \frac{dy}{du}\frac{du}{dt}$$
$$= \frac{d}{du}(\cos u)\frac{d}{dt}(2t - \theta)$$
$$= -\sin u \times 2 = -2\sin(2t - \theta).$$

Similarly, we need to differentiate $y = \sin u$, where $u = 2t - \theta$. Applying the Composite Rule, we have

$$\frac{dy}{dt} = \frac{dy}{du}\frac{du}{dt}$$
$$= \frac{d}{du}(\sin u)\frac{d}{dt}(2t - \theta)$$
$$= \cos u \times 2 = 2\cos(2t - \theta).$$

(b) From the acceleration function

$$\frac{dv}{dt} = a = -50\sin(2t - \theta),$$

and using the first result from part (a), we have

$$v = \int(-50\sin(2t - \theta))\,dt = 25\cos(2t - \theta) + c,$$

where c is an arbitrary constant. Since $v = 10\sqrt{6}$ when $t = 0$, and

$$\theta = \arcsin(\tfrac{1}{5}) = \arccos(\tfrac{2}{5}\sqrt{6}),$$

we find that

$$10\sqrt{6} = 25\cos(-\arccos(\tfrac{2}{5}\sqrt{6})) + c$$
$$= 25 \times \tfrac{2}{5}\sqrt{6} + c;$$

that is, $c = 0$. Hence the velocity function is

$$v = 25\cos(2t - \theta).$$

(c) From the velocity function for $ds/dt = v$ just found, and using the second result from part (a), we have

$$s = \int 25\cos(2t - \theta)\,dt = 12.5\sin(2t - \theta) + c,$$

where c is an arbitrary constant. Since $s = 30$ when $t = 0$, we find that

$$30 - 12.5\sin(-\arcsin(\tfrac{1}{5})) + c$$
$$= 12.5 \times (-\tfrac{1}{5}) + c;$$

that is, $c = 32.5$. Hence the position function is

$$s = 12.5\sin(2t - \theta) + 32.5.$$

(d) The largest value of $s = 12.5\sin(2t - \theta) + 32.5$ occurs when $\sin(2t - \theta) = 1$, and is therefore 45. So the length of the bungee at full stretch is 45 metres.

(e) The largest value of $|a| = 50|\sin(2t - \theta)|$ occurs when $|\sin(2t - \theta)| = 1$ and is therefore $50\,\mathrm{m\,s^{-2}}$ (that is, 5 times the acceleration due to gravity). Now $\sin(2t - \theta) = 1$ corresponds to the maximum value 45 m for s (whereas $\sin(2t - \theta) = -1$ does not occur while the bungee is stretched), so that the largest magnitude of acceleration is experienced where the bungee has its maximum extension.

Solution 4.1

(a) An integral of $\cos(5x) + 2\sin(5x)$ is $\frac{1}{5}\sin(5x) - \frac{2}{5}\cos(5x)$, so we have

$$\int_0^{\pi/4} (\cos(5x) + 2\sin(5x))\, dx$$
$$= \left[\tfrac{1}{5}\sin(5x) - \tfrac{2}{5}\cos(5x) \right]_0^{\pi/4}$$
$$= \left(\tfrac{1}{5}\sin(\tfrac{5}{4}\pi) - \tfrac{2}{5}\cos(\tfrac{5}{4}\pi) \right) - \left(\tfrac{1}{5}\sin 0 - \tfrac{2}{5}\cos 0 \right)$$
$$= \tfrac{1}{5}\left(-1/\sqrt{2} - 2\left(-1/\sqrt{2} \right) - (-2) \right)$$
$$= \tfrac{1}{5}\left(1/\sqrt{2} + 2 \right) \simeq 0.541.$$

(b) An integral of $6u^{-2}$ is $-6u^{-1}$, so we have

$$\int_1^2 \frac{6}{u^2}\, du = \left[-\frac{6}{u} \right]_1^2$$
$$= -\tfrac{6}{2} - \left(-\tfrac{6}{1} \right) = 3.$$

(c) Using the integral given, we have

$$\int_0^\pi e^t \sin t\, dt$$
$$= \left[\tfrac{1}{2}e^t(\sin t - \cos t) \right]_0^\pi$$
$$= \tfrac{1}{2}e^\pi(\sin\pi - \cos\pi) - \tfrac{1}{2}e^0(\sin 0 - \cos 0)$$
$$= \tfrac{1}{2}(-(-1)e^\pi - (-1))$$
$$= \tfrac{1}{2}(e^\pi + 1) \simeq 12.1.$$

Solution 4.2

(a) Since $2x^3 > 0$ for $1 \le x \le 2$, the area required is

$$\int_1^2 2x^3\, dx = \left[\tfrac{1}{2}x^4 \right]_1^2$$
$$= \tfrac{1}{2} \times 2^4 - \tfrac{1}{2} \times 1^4$$
$$= \tfrac{1}{2}(2^4 - 1) = \tfrac{15}{2}.$$

(b) If $0 < x < 3$, then we have both $x > 0$ and $3 > x$, that is, $3 - x > 0$. Hence $x(3 - x)$ is the product of two positive factors, so $x(3-x) > 0$.

The graph of $y = x(3-x)$ is a parabola which cuts the x-axis at $x = 0$ and $x = 3$. As just shown, this graph is above the x-axis for $0 < x < 3$. Thus the area required is the area under the graph of $y = x(3-x)$ from $x = 0$ to $x = 3$, which is

$$\int_0^3 x(3-x)\, dx = \int_0^3 (3x - x^2)\, dx$$
$$= \left[\tfrac{3}{2}x^2 - \tfrac{1}{3}x^3 \right]_0^3$$
$$= \tfrac{3}{2} \times 3^2 - \tfrac{1}{3} \times 3^3$$
$$= \tfrac{27}{2} - 9 = \tfrac{9}{2}.$$

(c) Since $1/(1+x^2) > 0$ for all x, the area required is

$$\int_{-2}^2 \frac{1}{1+x^2}\, dx = [\arctan x]_{-2}^2 \quad \text{(given)}$$
$$= \arctan 2 - \arctan(-2)$$
$$= 2\arctan 2 \simeq 2.21.$$

Solution 4.3

(a) The area of a circle with radius zero is zero, so that $A(0) = 0$.

(b) The annulus is obtained by removing a circle of radius r from a circle of radius $r + h$. Hence its area may be written as $A(r+h) - A(r)$.

(c) The area of the annulus is approximated by that of a rectangle with length $2\pi r$ and width h, which has area $2\pi rh$.

(d) From parts (b) and (c), we have

$$A(r+h) - A(r) \simeq 2\pi rh.$$

On dividing by h and then taking the limit as $h \to 0$, this becomes

$$\lim_{h \to 0} \left(\frac{A(r+h) - A(r)}{h} \right) = 2\pi r.$$

The left-hand side is the derivative of $A(r)$, so we have

$$A'(r) = 2\pi r,$$

as required.

(e) Integration gives

$$A(r) = \int 2\pi r\, dr = \pi r^2 + c,$$

where c is an arbitrary constant. On putting $r = 0$ and using the result of part (a), we find that $c = 0$, so that $A(r) = \pi r^2$ $(0 \le r \le R)$. In particular, we deduce that $A(R) = \pi R^2$.

Index